PRIME TIME WOMAN

Also by Cherry Marshall:
Fashion Modelling as a Career
The Cat-Walk

PRIME TIME WOMAN

A GUIDE TO LOOKING AND FEELING GREAT ALL YOUR LIFE

CHERRY MARSHALL

SIDGWICK & JACKSON
LONDON

First published in Great Britain in
1986 by Sidgwick & Jackson Limited
1 Tavistock Chambers, Bloomsbury Way
London WC1A 2SG

Black and white illustrations by Annie Hutchison

Designed by Karen Mack, Grid Graphics

ISBN 0–283–99360–X hardcover
ISBN 0–283–99462–2 softcover

Phototypeset by Falcon Graphic Art Limited
Wallington, Surrey
Printed in Great Britain by
R.J. Acford, Industrial Estate, Chichester, Sussex

To Sarah (who stopped me **talking** *about the book and made me* **write** *it) Vida and Jemilah.*
And to my mother, who still keeps me on my toes.

CONTENTS

INTRODUCTION 9

INTRODUCING THE NEW ERA 11

LOOKING GOOD 23

YOUR BODY 61

WALKING TALL 97

DRESSING WITH STYLE 115

INTRODUCTION

In the beginning, about twenty-five years ago, it was the Older Woman of thirty who suddenly came into her own. It was suggested that perhaps she was *still* attractive, and could show her younger sisters a thing or two. She may not have the figure or the youthful looks of an eighteen year old, but she had a certain mature something that appealed quite definitely to young boys and older men.

And then, out of the blue, the *really* Older Woman – of forty – emerged, battling for recognition of her super-fit body, stunning good looks and incomparable sex appeal. 'You too can look young and beautiful,' she told us in her lavishly illustrated beauty book, and the neglected, dejected middle-aged women of the Western world gave grateful thanks to Fonda, Loren, Collins, Welch, and the other famous beauties.

But time inevitably moved on and some of the forty year olds found themselves at the half century mark. And what happened? Joan Collins and Sophia Loren found themselves competing for the title of THE WORLD'S MOST GLAMOROUS WOMAN.

How wonderful, they said, to be fifty!

So what comes next? I'm in my early sixties, and I've never felt better – and I know many women who feel the same. We are not concerned with capturing any glamour titles, but we know that we are attractive women with no plans to retire into old age for the foreseeable future.

For here we are, at the beginning of a new era, the era of the dynamic, confident, experienced and fascinating older woman. I wanted to write this book to tell those of you who hadn't heard the good news that this is *our* time for looking good and leading full, exciting lives.

I'll tell you right away what kind of book this isn't. It isn't the sort of beauty book that makes me, at least, feel defeated before I even start: the kind that promises you physical perfection if you perform each exercise every day, follow the diet to the letter, and dedicate yourself to the pursuit of beauty at the expense of everything else. That is selling dreams. Even the few able to make such a commitment are unlikely to end up looking like the woman on the cover unless they were born with all her natural assets.

You know, as I do, that perfection is not necessary to make a woman attractive, sexy, even beautiful. I am going to tell you how you can look marvellous just the way you are. The exercise and diet information is there if you don't feel happy with yourself – but I know at least one woman, two-and-a-half stone 'overweight', who will ignore it. She's my age, revels in her size, and is constantly pursued by men.

More important, I think, is knowing how to dress, make-up and carry yourself so that you look the best you can starting from *today*. As you get older you must change – you don't want to be stuck in the style you adopted in your twenties – but neither do you want to label yourself 'old' by your clothes, mannerisms or attitude. I can show you ways of looking good and youthful, while avoiding that dreadful 'mutton dressed as lamb' tag. For we are all staying younger longer, as well as living longer, and I see no reason why we shouldn't look terrific and enjoy every minute of it.

On my talks round the country, talking to women about beauty care and fashion know-how, I'm always asked the same thing. Why isn't the older woman catered for in the same way as the young middle-aged? They go on to say that it's probably too late anyhow, that nobody cares what they look like and that they're perfectly happy as they are – which is blatantly untrue. They lap up advice and information hungrily. Their vanity and self esteem are still there, just waiting for a late blossoming. The nagging fear of looking 'tarty', like 'mutton dressed as lamb', or even that 'people will laugh at me' is a reflection of the general attitude to older women. No wonder they are embarrassed to ask for advice at beauty counters, or that they hang around the more exciting clothes in the local store before dragging themselves off to the drab, old ladies' department. Their natural desire to look and feel attractive is quashed from the start. They haven't the confidence to battle with young assistants because they don't know what they are looking for, and their answer to raised eyebrows is usually, 'I'm just looking, thank you.'

No wonder they complain about the state of their skin, their figures, or the way they look generally. They lavish far more care on their houses, pets, gardens and members of the family than they ever do on themselves. It doesn't have to be like that. The point is – what to do about it.

I like the challenge. I like living in the present and doing things that give me an immediate lift, without wondering what the effects will be in twenty years' time. I have enough experience to know what I want. I've got the confidence to know what to wear and what suits me best. I don't get worked up about what is in fashion – but I also know how not to look old-fashioned. I know what colours suit me, the shapes that flatter my figure, the accessories that transform an outfit.

This is something that all women can learn – and should learn. Because older women have a very positive statement to make about fashion and beauty. We are the living proof of all that has ever been written about the effects of 'taking care of yourself'. We are the buttress against all that is tatty, ungroomed, freakish and unflattering in the relentless, over-commercialised tide of fashion.

The attractive older woman, with her discreet make-up, cared-for hair and well-groomed clothes is a reassuring figure at a time when most fashion writers have little knowledge of what looking *good* is all about.

The older, confident woman, can hold her place in the world. And not only in the way she looks. As Dr Leslie Libow, Chief of Geriatric Medicine at the City Hospital Centre, New York says, 'The older brain is far from being diminished in capacity. It is actually a strong, experienced, intelligent and well-nourished organ.'

INTRODUCING THE NEW ERA

WHY BEING AN OLDER WOMAN IS SOMETHING TO ENJOY

Remember the Oscar Wilde joke that youth was wasted on the young? That may be so, but I increasingly think that maturity is wasted on the mature.

The young may not take advantage of their youth, but neither do we make the most of the good things we have accumulated or take advantage of our opportunity to lead a rich and rewarding life.

For some, reaching a landmark age, such as fifty or sixty, means the start of new and exciting pursuits. Others simply accept the out-dated myth that everything is rapidly running downhill. They never look on the positive side about what they have gained, they dwell only on what they believe they have 'lost'.

You have the choice. Do you want a life that is vivid and interesting, with yourself as a central, attractive, active participant? I do – and I believe it is possible for every one of us who really wants to make the effort.

I love Claudette Colbert's attitude to life. While starring in a musical recently in London, she was asked for the secret of her vitality. Although well into her eighties she replied that she didn't give a thought to her age but continued to live as she'd always done – to the full. 'Once you start thinking about your age,' she added, 'you're on the way to being old'. That's a philosophy I agree with: the secret is to disregard your age, not consider it a handicap.

Another actress who feels the same way is Evelyn Laye. At eighty-five, playing Fairy Christabel in a pantomime, she insisted she doesn't believe in age at all. She likes to reverse the number – to fifty-eight – which is what she feels is about right!

So this book is not for the woman who feels life is behind her. It is for the woman who intends to continue to enjoy it in all its aspects. Confident and outgoing, she knows there are exciting experiences ahead and she is ready for the good things life has to offer.

I'm not naïve enough to believe that we automatically like being the older woman. It's something we must prepare ourselves for, and this process often begins at a very early age – as does a negative attitude to growing older. Girls often moan that they're no longer young after their twenty-first birthday. For others, thirty is the end, particularly if they have no husband or baby. Forty is a disaster! There simply is no life after forty!

But at fifty something rather ominous happens. Even those who have maintained a fairly balanced attitude towards ageing start to get in on the act. Everyone, it seems, agrees that fifty really *is* old, and that from there on it's only downhill. This is the idea that I want to challenge, because it is untrue, unfair – and silly! This is the era of the older woman, and all of us have plenty of good times to come – but to experience them it is necessary to believe it.

AVOIDING THE STEROTYPES

During the many years in which I ran a grooming school for older women I had first-hand experience of what made them feel insecure. Nearly all of them thought that because they were no longer young they were 'finished'. They didn't think they had the possibil-

ity to be attractive or admired anymore and a lot of the fun had gone out of their lives.

Middle age had become synonymous with the menopause, overweight, sexlessness, dullness – and husbands who looked for younger women. They were ill-at-ease and felt dowdy when in the company of younger women, which pushed them deeper into depression at a time when they were potentially more interesting and better-looking than before.

I knew exactly how they felt because at a much earlier age I had gone through the same thing. I was only twenty at the time. The war was on and I'd just had my first baby. My husband was abroad and I was living with my mother, and there was no doubt about it, I was depressed. I felt old, unattractive, and finished. My figure had changed and after months of wearing horrible outsize clothes because there was no such thing as maternity wear, I had no idea what to wear to make myself look better.

What was the point anyway, I thought, if I'm only going to push a pram and never go out? My mother was impatient that I should yearn to look the way that I had just a year or so before.

'You ought to be more concerned with looking like a married woman and a mother', she said. I assumed that she was correct, that I no longer had a 'right' to be concerned about being an attractive woman.

Well, I was lucky because I got out of that trap. Four years later I was modelling in London, and I had realised that there was nothing incompatible about being a wife and mother *and* an attractive woman. But I can truthfully say that I've never felt so old in my life as I did then. I looked at least ten years older too. My feelings were reflected in my face, in the way I walked and in my whole attitude to life.

This is what can happen to women at any age. At a certain point they give

up – believing that it is wrong or ridiculous to want to be attractive. That's when they are likely to 'become' whatever they believe is consistent with the age they are. Many women put on a lot of weight because they believe it is 'normal' to do so after a certain age. They stop making an effort with the way they look because they believe there's 'no point' any more. They allow themselves to develop ageing habits in the way they speak, dress and present themselves. They stop trying new things or keeping an open mind. In other words, they *make* themselves old.

I fell into that trap when I was twenty, and I learnt my lesson then – I hope that I never forget it. And I believe that every older woman can look and feel good if she wants to. In other chapters I tell you about what you can do to revolutionize your physical appearance. But that is by no means all that is involved. Think about whether you are behaving in the kind of stereotyped way that allows people to label you as old – and makes you feel old. Ageing habits can creep up on you unawares.

Here are some ways I think you can start to break those habits.

• Don't think in terms of age. How many years you've lived is not important – it's what you do and how you behave that counts.

• Don't say things like 'At my age. . . .' or 'Now I'm getting old. . .' or refer to your age in a derogatory way. It's not only embarrassing for the listener (who feels obliged to say patronising things like 'Oh, you don't look so old. . .') but it also gives you a dangerous excuse for avoiding anything challenging or difficult – and that's where excitement and fun are to be found.

• Develop a healthy ego. Don't think it's unimportant to spend time on yourself. Believe it or not, your family and friends enjoy your company more if

Left: A fabulous eighty-five year old showing that you can be attractive as a woman all through your life. Here is Claudette Colbert coming out of the Savoy Hotel after her successful appearance in a West End show.

From my early teens I was always immensely flattered when I was told how much like her I looked. I hope I have the good fortune to look as she does when I am eighty-five.

you are busy and interested, even if it means you have less time for them individually. Someone who feels she is not worth bothering about gives others exactly the same feeling.

● Do one different thing every day, even if it's only taking a different route to the shops or wearing a new lipstick.

● Don't settle for an inactive, indoor life. 'If you don't use it, you lose it' is a basic truth. The less you do, the less you will feel able to do — and that's what makes you feel old.

● Do something positive whenever you catch yourself in a gloomy mood. Allowing yourself to brood achieves nothing.

● Add a cheerful colour to whatever you're wearing. You'll be amazed at what a morale booster it can be.

● Keep a smile on your face, not a scowl. Facial expressions can be a result of habit — not just a reflection of mood. Frowning when you're angry is one thing. Frowning all the time is quite another.

● Wipe 'As I always say. . .' from your vocabulary. If you always say it then you've stopped thinking. Keep an open mind. Listen to other people. Change your newspaper to get another point of view.

● Get books from the library and read, as a change from watching television.

● Get out of the house and walk. Take an interest in what is going on around you.

● Try going back to school. Join a day or evening class on a subject that appeals to you.

● Don't turn down invitations be-cause you can't be bothered to go. Even if it turns out to be a flop, it's a change of routine — and stimulating.

● Don't feel you have to keep up a frantic pace — but don't settle down to an easy life either.

● If you no longer have a daily routine that you must keep to, don't sleep too long or think you need more sleep than before. Get up early — before nine — have a short nap after lunch, and don't go to bed too early.

● Take pride in your appearance al-ways. Never think it doesn't matter.

● Keep in touch with friends. A post-card or telephone call is often all that's needed if they live far away, and you don't have to do any elaborate enter-taining for those that live near. Be open to the possibility of making new friends.

● Don't forget how to laugh! It makes difficulties easier to cope with. Laugh and the world laughs with you. . . . . .

THE OLDER WOMAN'S REVOLUTION

It's been a long time coming, but now it's here. Most of us are tired of being lumped together as O.A.P.'s and we demand far more than Getting On Clubs, Meals on Wheels, travel passes and pensions. We want recognition that we are a constructive and energetic force in society. A few women are already showing this to be true — it is now up to the rest of us to follow.

As Mary Warnock pointed out in an article in *The Guardian* '. . . with the present population trend and the general longevity of women there are more and more of us in this neglected age group. Most articles written see a steady, and hopefully graceful, decline into old age with all frivolities a thing

Left: She loves clothes, make-up and all the trimmings and at eighty-five Evelyn Laye is as interested in her appearance and her work in the theatre as she's ever been. 'I'm far too busy to think about my age,' she says, 'I've got far too much to do. Just reverse my age to 58 and you've got it about right.'

of the past . . . In real life, however, there are many women who are old and busy, old and powerful, old and energetic and old and elegant.'

But we've come a long way since I had my grooming school in the early sixties. That was aimed at the woman of thirty and over, when anyone over the age of sixteen was thought to have one foot in the grave. At the time my critics laughed and said it was ludicrous to have classes for over-thirties, implying they were not worth bothering with.

Now no-one would dare to think like that, but many people are still prepared to say that there is a 'cut-off' age, after which you are simply old. Everything is relative. I remember an extraordinary woman I met during a lecture tour who was impatient with me for talking about middle age as 'getting on'. 'Why, you're in the full bloom of your life,' she said. 'When you get to my age you can think of slowing down a bit – although I'm off on a motoring tour of Europe next month. Driving myself.' She was eighty-four.

My mother, at eighty-six, still knits herself fashionable jumpers. She broke her arm badly twenty years ago and was told it would never heal well enough to hold a needle again. 'What nonsense!' she said at the time. 'If I want to knit, I'll knit and nobody will tell me what I can't do'.

Margaret Mead, the anthropologist and most liberated of women, wrote many years ago '. . . the reproductive years are a block to creativity'. For those of us who were constantly worried about pregnancy and have devoted lots of time and energy to bringing up our children, middle age means a new beginning.

It all depends on how you approach it. A friend I was discussing this book with said she found the whole subject very depressing. 'I can see nothing good in old age,' she said, 'there is only deterioration'. She is in her seventies, and she'd felt that way from quite an early age.

What bad luck, I thought. She is such good company, loves and wears beautiful clothes, and has many varied interests. She is a pleasure to be with – but she only looks at the negative side of 'old age'.

'Do you find it depressing to be with me now that I'm no longer young?' I asked.

'Oh no!' she replied, 'You're still young!'

That is when I realised that youth to her had always belonged to those who were ten years or so her junior. When she had been my age she had felt old – but she could now see that she had been no such thing. Even as we were talking, my aunt – of the same age as my friend – was off on her second honeymoon with the full blessing of her six children and innumerable grandchildren. The main difference between them is that my aunt has no intention of feeling, acting or being thought old.

BEING OLDER DOESN'T MEAN LESS ATTRACTIVE

One of the reasons women feel depressed as they get older is because they worry about their looks, and fall into the habit of comparing themselves with women years younger – or with themselves at a younger age. It's pointless. Getting and looking older is not something that is unique to you. As you age, so do your contemporaries. I find that when I go to parties there are plenty of men who want to talk and flirt with me. I may be older – but so are they.

We're all in a constant state of change from the time we're born, and once you accept this rather than hanging on to the past you start to look as good as you should. Worrying about age or striving to disguise the fact that you are growing older is unattractive. A woman who *is* relaxed and confident about herself is attractive – and she doesn't have to be a beauty, or young.

It's the inner vitality and confidence that transforms an 'ordinary' woman into someone we admire and want to be with, and these qualities can increase as we get older. Ali MacGraw, the American actress, has a message to herself pinned up on the wall, 'I don't mind getting older. I'm feeling better about myself all the time. I don't want to be any age other than the age I am now.'

We are lucky to have access to everything we need to help us to look good. Hairdressers, beauty advisers, health clubs, magazines, books on health care and diets, records and tapes on relaxing and exercise. We can keep up-to-date with all aspects of personal wellbeing to help us reach each new decade in good health and looking as good as we can.

Part of the problem is that women confuse looking younger than their age with attractiveness. I aim to look the best I can at the age I am *now*. I don't frantically pursue ways to make myself look younger – just good.

We are so often our own worst enemies, complaining we are old and making ourselves miserable peering into mirrors to look at a face we no longer like. There's a very simple answer to that – don't keep examining yourself in mirrors! Make yourself look as good as you can and then forget about it. Tell yourself you are an attractive woman – and believe it. That's what I do and it makes me feel confident. I feel good and that impression is conveyed to others.

Of the many letters I've received, one particular one stays in my mind. It was from a woman who'd read an article I wrote for a woman's magazine. She wrote:

'I've never been a beauty and I've always looked older than my age. I've never felt very happy about myself, but now at seventy I feel it couldn't matter less. Why should I start dressing myself up and putting on make-up?'

What was obvious to me was that she *did* care otherwise she wouldn't have bothered to write. I wrote back:

'If you have time to spare, why not spend it on yourself? You're entitled to spoil yourself and it's a great morale booster. Make a fuss of yourself. The more you care for yourself the better you will feel in every way. Seventy is no age to give up caring. If you have never made much of an effort in the way you look, you are in for a big surprise if you start now. You have the chance to look better now than ever before.'

Then I added some hints about things she could do immediately to enhance her appearance.

Some time later I was getting my things together after giving a lunchtime lecture, when I was approached by a woman I had noticed in the audience. She looked like someone who was hugely enjoying an amusing secret.

'I must thank you,' she said, and went on to introduce herself as my defeated correspondent. 'I booked myself an appointment with the hairdresser as soon as I got your letter,' she continued. 'That one gesture to myself showed me I did care what I looked like. Then I allowed myself to be dragged along with my granddaughter to a slimmer's group. Changing my appearance in very slight ways has made me feel better about everything – I still find it hard to believe! Isn't life exciting?' Her enthusiasm was so infectious that I found myself smiling all the way home. She wasn't the best-looking woman in the hall, she certainly wasn't the youngest or the most elegant, but she really stood out from the crowd. Her excitement and vitality, brought out by making small but substantial changes in her life had made her what she said she had never been before – an attractive woman.

PERENNIALLY GLAMOUROUS

One of the high prices that has to be paid by famous beauties is the chore of remaining for ever glamorous. Our interest and curiosity in them grows as we get older, and we watch them avidly on television just to see how they're ageing. We are lucky that no one subjects us to the same scrutiny!

'Doesn't she look old!' we often say. 'I reckon she has more wrinkles than me!'

And the poor woman is judged entirely by the number of lines she has, by the droop of her jawline and the texture of her skin. As if ageing was an atrocious sin she had committed. It is bad enough that the heavy studio make-up and hot penetrating lights fatten and age by their very nature without the armchair critics sitting at home making their own derogatory assessment.

Television is unkind. The stars look much better in real life, off screen. But some of them still look better than others, even in that unkind mirror, and I have tried to analyse why this is.

I have realised that it is the person who desperately hangs on to the image she had in the past who comes off worst – even if she 'looks good for her age'. For it is when you are a carbon copy of your younger self – except older – that unkind comparisons are made.

I recently watched a Royal Command Performance on television, with nostalgia as its theme. It confirmed what I thought about not trying to stand still. It's not just a case of constantly changing our image and keeping up-to-date with current trends in make-up and dress. It means seeing ourselves in a realistic light and making the most of what we see.

Of the stars who took part that evening I was particularly impressed by Lauren Bacall who looked relaxed and cool (but isn't she always?) in a simple long-sleeved jersey dress. Glamorous, yes, and still wearing her hair in that famous style, but there was no embarassing over-made-up face or self-conscious preening. She looked as if she'd grown comfortably into her age and liked it. The late Grace Kelly had the same quality and innate sense of style which was universally admired.

By contrast there were the 'perennially glamorous' stars who remain older versions of their former Hollywood selves. Not an ounce of surplus weight, a mass of peroxide-blonde hair and heavy make-up. By virtue of an unchanging image you are irresistibly reminded of the fact that they have become very much older. Better by far, is to put on that little extra weight, tone down the make-up and throw away the false eyelashes.

But we shouldn't forget that stars must be larger than life – and even when it works for them, to attempt to imitate them in our own daily life is asking for trouble. To learn something from them is another matter.

Take Joan Collins, for example, the current leader of the pack of older glamorous women. When she made her entrance on the Command Performance show a wave of excitement swept through the audience. A defiant fifty-two, looking thirty, she was positively bursting with glamour in her fur-trimmed sequined gown.

'She doesn't really look like that,' someone watching with me said.

'Oh yes she does,' I replied.

I'd met her a few years previously when her *Beauty Book* was published and I'd been asked to talk about it on the STV programme *Houseparty*. I wanted to remind her that she'd belonged to the model agency I took over in the early fifties, but I also wanted to have a really close look at her! All I can say is that she didn't appear to have a line on her face, or baggy eyes or a drooping jaw line – *and* she said she didn't believe in face-lifts either. Face-lifts or not, she has been the most talked-about 'goddess' ever since she was voted the world's most glamorous woman, when she was in her forties. You may not admire the way she looks, but there is no denying that she is a

Right: The distinctive thing about Lauren Bacall is that you always notice her first and the clothes afterwards – the first rule of classic dressing. Now in her sixties, she looks uncluttered, confident, with no over-dressing or straining to look younger – which invariably has the opposite effect. She wears just a few pieces of eye-catching jewellery but nothing too distracting. That is the secret of mature elegance.

present-day phenomenom. She defies age on all counts — figure, face, confidence and a life style that includes a new, much younger husband. The very expression on her face, that mocking half smile, dares anyone to fault the way she looks. How many women twenty years younger can hold a candle to her?

But the mistake many women make is to believe that if it works for her it will work for them. That kind of glamour, which involves a lifetime of dedicated work on face and body, is not just a question of a hairstyle and the right make-up. It can't, and shouldn't, be copied in normal everyday life. That's why other women I talk to are at a loss. They are attracted by the beauty and exercise books they see on the shelves — because they want to look

like the woman on the cover. They become downhearted when they read just what it is they are supposed to do to achieve this, and many believe it is, anyway, 'too late' for them. That is why some women cease to bother, and why in this book I am concerned to tell you the things that can really work for you — sometimes instantly!

It's not surprising we're often accused of sour grapes. Millions of women make themselves miserable because they don't look like the models in fashion magazines and beauty books, or like their favourite TV actress. When I was an agent I was always being asked what the models *really* looked like. It didn't seem possible that they could be as flawless as in their photographs, and of course they weren't. The cameras can be lovingly kind to photogenic faces, but nobody looks good all the time.

So we shouldn't kid ourselves that someone like Joan Collins is just lucky. Her approach to herself is thoroughly professional and as she says in her book she is, 'coiffed and cosmeticised to the nines for the film cameras'. But behind it all she gives enormous care to the upkeep of her health and looks. We should be grateful to her. She refuses to be pushed into the stereotyped role of a middle-aged woman. She has looks, a magnificent figure, and abounding confidence, and she has the unenviable job of parading it all in front of the world's spotlights.

I'm very curious to see how she progresses into her sixties, when perhaps her role in *Dynasty* is over. She knows what looking good is all about, so the heavy make-up and doll-like wigs will surely go, together with the very dark hair. As we get older our skin changes colour and unnaturally dark hair looks harsh by comparison. Nature knows what she's doing when hair fades to complement the skin. It doesn't mean we have to be grey, or pepper-and-salt, or 'washed out'. Once the hair fades we have 'free' streaks which can be highlighted with golden or ash shampoos and washed out again.

ATTAINING VITALITY

It is not the number of lines on your face that make you 'old': neither is it the absence of them that makes you attractive.

This was brought home to me yet again at a party I went to the other week. By far the most glamorous and beautiful woman there was in her early forties. She was very slim and expensively dressed, and had obviously spent a long time preparing for the party. But she had no presence, animation or glow. It was like looking at a photograph rather than a real person. She moved slowly, she sat down whenever she could. She looked bored when anyone started to chat to her. I eventually spoke to her myself, and she soon opened up. As I had suspected, she was unhappy. Something had happened that had confirmed her feeling that she was growing 'old'. 'I used to be a beautiful woman,' she told me wryly. 'But you are!' I said, despite knowing that nothing I could say would help her at the time. But the truth was that the way she was feeling about herself affected the image she presented to the world. The way she moved, her glum expression, her air of defeat totally detracted from her beauty. She looked, if not old, no longer young.

In contrast there was another woman at the same party, considerably older, who did not have any of this woman's natural assets — but it couldn't have mattered less to the people who gathered around her. She had a natural vivacity that was infectious. She was enjoying herself, clearly confident without being vain. I was particularly impressed by the way she walked and held herself: she was supple and 'young' in every movement. I asked her if she exercised regularly, 'Never!' she replied, 'I don't have the time, I'm always rushing about.'

It seemed irrelevant to speculate on how old she was: she exuded vitality. It reminded me once again that vitality is the X ingredient that offers youth at any age.

'It's all very well talking about vitality,' an ex-model friend of mine complained, 'but I haven't yet found a pill that makes me want to jump over the moon. What do you take that makes you so active?'

'I take my bottom out of the chair and get moving,' I replied. She tucked her feet comfortably under her as she curled up on the sofa.

'But look at the weather! Where is there to go on a day like this? I feel like getting under the bed clothes and going to sleep. I haven't got the use of the car anyway. Although I suppose I could get my hair done'.

'That would be better than sitting here moping,' I agreed, 'But isn't there anything you'd really love to do?'

'Not on a day like this,' she replied.

I could have had a conversation with her like this any day of the year. It would either be too hot, too cold, too windy or too wet. There's no such thing as bad weather, I tried telling her, only different kinds of weather. But at fifty she was bored with her life. There were plenty of things she could do but she felt 'too old'. What she wanted were the things of her youth: love affairs, night clubs, dancing, socialising — but she wanted them as a *young woman*, and she'd convinced herself they didn't belong to middle age. With a third of her life ahead of her she'd already opted out.

I suggested she tried something new. 'Make things happen,' I said. 'While you sit around complaining about the age you are and brooding on the past, things can only get worse. Once you decide that it is up to you to make your life interesting and start doing new things, you will start to feel good about yourself.'

She looked at me in amazement. The

thought of not relying on pills was indeed new to her.

'But *you* always take vitamin C and E and bran and goodness knows what,' she accused me.

'Yes, I know. But they never replace the efforts I make myself.'

It wasn't that I didn't sympathise with her. It's the easiest thing in the world to slip into a depressed frame of mind – but it's also possible to change your attitude if the desire is there. I often think of Adolph Zukor, the founder of Paramount Studios, who said on his 100th birthday 'If I'd known how old I was gong to be I'd have taken better care of myself'. Imagine what he would have said to a woman half his age who complained of feeling old!

I know how I felt when I closed my business after almost thirty years of a busy working life. I was fifty-two, and I wrote a book about the modelling world called *The Catwalk*. At the end I wrote 'Now I have the leisure I've dreamed about for so long. Tea in the afternoons and window shopping. Weekends with my granddaughter making cakes, washing doll clothes in the sink, trying out the sewing machine, collecting conkers in the park. . .'

Yes, it was lovely, a dream come true after what seemed a lifetime with hardly a moment for myself. But it wasn't enough to keep an active mind and body in peak condition. Although I was appearing regularly in a television programme there was a large gap in my life. I told myself I'd earned this rest, that I should sit back and take it easy. The trouble was that after taking it easy for a short time I wasn't tired any more.

I'd potter about the flat, then wander off to the shops looking for something I fancied for lunch or supper. I found myself daydreaming about the past, dwelling on my 'exciting' career or thinking about the children when they were young. A shapeless kind of life which lasted for about a year, during which time it began to dawn on me that if I didn't think seriously about the way I was going to spend the next twenty or thirty years of my life I was in trouble.

My 'rest' was not giving me energy, it was draining it away. If I wanted to retain the vitality that I prized in myself and admired in others I would have to do something positive about it. Among other things, I contacted like-minded friends, arranged trips to theatres, exhibitions and art galleries, re-kindled a long standing love affair. That was just the beginning. Time running out? I'd never had so much of it in my life!

Doctors agree that ageing is accelerated by physical and mental inactivity. The busier we are, the younger we will be in mind and body. The trouble is, we are surrounded by all the mod. cons. which take the hard work out of everything but nevertheless leave us feeling inexplicably weary. Taking the car or bus everywhere spoils the chance of having a good exhilarating walk. The same pattern of inactivity often applies to the mind. Stagnation is the result, and we become boring, repetitious, stuck-in-the-mud and defeated.

Later in the book I'll tell you some painless ways to get your body moving in a young way – you'll be surprised to find how energising it is. Our own vitality may be temporarily buried – but it is there, just waiting to be released.

It isn't age alone that influences the way we look. At any age we can have a youthful appearance without striving to be young. What are the main ingredients? Vivacity? An outgoing personality? Confidence? An agile body? Discreet, clever make-up? The right hairstyle? A slim figure? An open mind and interest in what's going on? Stylish clothes? It can be all or any of these things. It is usually simply a case of finding what works for *you*, and in the following chapters I will help you to discover your own particular formula.

LOOKING GOOD

'How does it feel', I was often asked when I had my model agency, 'being surrounded by all those beautiful models? It must be awfully depressing – they get younger and younger each year. Doesn't it make you feel pretty ancient?'

Other women were often surprised that my answer was, 'No!' because that is how they thought they would have felt themselves.

In fact, being surrounded by perfect good looks can have quite the opposite effect. Very pretty girls who had nothing else to offer became very boring after a while. Except in a professional sense I stopped noticing how they looked and didn't consider them to be particularly attractive. That is how my staff felt too. We had one top girl who was very unpleasant – it became hard to look at her and reverently think 'oh, Beauty'!

On the other hand, the girls with warmth and personality remained good-looking in the eyes of all of us who worked in the agency.

I've found that this is even more the case among 'non-models'. I am a great believer in, 'you get the face you deserve'. An unattractive personality has a way of imposing itself upon the most beautiful features so they become increasingly unappealing and even plain.

Intelligence, personality, warmth and good humour shine out of a face, whatever its age. As the years go by, the texture of your skin and the shape of your features has less to do with beauty than the person behind them. I have one very good friend of whom people always say, 'Now, *she* must have been a beauty when young.' In fact, she was no such thing. Her face is large-featured, so that when she was young she always looked older than her age. She had rather oily skin, and suffered from spots and open pores. But as the years have gone by she has 'grown into' her face: that large–boned look ages very well. Her skin has dried out, and because oily skin is tougher than dry skin her face has hardly lined. But it is the fact that she is interesting and interested in everything around her that gives her the special quality that some people call beauty.

One thing is certain. There is hardly a woman who doesn't feel she'd like to do something to improve the way she looks. We know that our skin will age, attention or not, but nobody wants it to age before its time and we want it to age not only slowly but as little as possible. And the truth is that care is rewarded and neglect demands its price.

In this chapter I am going to set out a care and beauty routine that really works. The essence is simplicity and a simple routine is just as effective as a more complicated one. For most of us it is *more* effective because it is easier to stick to. If looking after your skin means an hour-long ritual every evening, then the temptation to do nothing at all is likely to take over.

Because the range of skin products is so vast and the advice so conflicting you often feel you need a beauty course before you know where to begin. Magazine beauty articles, like fashion ones, can be misleading. If I had a beauty column I would want to run the same advice every other month. There is so rarely anything really new in skincare that beauty editors must often despair. In fact, some of them merely rewrite the 'handouts' they receive from the cosmetic manufacturers. Reading, month after month, about 'revolutionary' new creams makes us feel we should be rushing out and buying them if we want to keep in good condition.

In actual fact it's like getting together a basic wardrobe – you only need a few indispensables, a sound working knowledge of what to do with what and a simple routine. The only rule after that is that you have to be consistent. It's no good stopping and starting and then complaining it's a waste of money because it doesn't do anything for you!

I meet many women at my shows who have never grasped the fact that they must get down to taking care of themselves. They want me to wave a magic wand and make it all happen for them – preferably with one jar of magic cream. It seems too easy (and yet too difficult!) for them to do it themselves.

They look for the hidden catch, or say they haven't the time.

SKINCARE BASICS

Many beauty books show you a cross-section of the skin and tell you how each dermatological layer works. I think that confuses the issue. There are three important things to know: skin should be cleansed properly, it should be protected from losing moisture, and it should be exfoliated, or 'stripped' regularly. As we become older it is less useful to classify the skin into the categories of oily, dry or sensitive. All but the very oiliest skins will become dry as the years go by, and the most sensible classification is delicate – which means that you have to treat your skin more gently than ever before.

CLEANSING

Even if you don't wear make-up, your skin needs to be properly cleansed – especially if you live in a city. If you don't clean thoroughly your skin looks dull and you may have problems if you put cream or make-up on top of badly cleansed skin.

The general rule is, cleanse your skin first thing in the morning, and last thing at night. Like all rules it can be broken, but only *very* occasionally. Once in a while, after a late night, it won't do any harm to wait till morning before cleansing.

It reminds me of one of my photographic models who did many soap commercials because of her beautiful skin. She was crazy about dancing and night clubs and often arrived home in the early hours of the morning, but exhausted as she was, she'd always take off every scrap of make-up before dropping into bed. No sooner had she fallen asleep than off would go her alarm – and she was back where she started, cleansing her face and putting back the make-up! One day, she made up her mind it was either to be early nights or an unclean face while she slept – and she settled for an unclean face. She still cleansed scrupulously twice a day: once when she woke, when she would take off all the stale make-up before applying a fresh lot, and once at the end of a working day, before applying her evening make-up. Certainly, while she was a model, she always looked wonderful and if anything did her any harm it was the lack of sleep. It wasn't that she had abandoned her cleansing and moisturizing routine, only shifted it to fit in to her lifestyle.

Another woman I know wanted to look good at bedtime for her husband. She used to put her make-up on in the evening, and remove it in the morning, and go round with an unmade-up face during the day.

Choice of Cleanser

Meticulous care of the skin is the top priority. As the years go by the skin gets thinner, so we need to treat it more gently. This is what is meant by 'slowing the ageing process'. Skin shouldn't be pulled and stretched either with rough towels, or hastily tissued-off creams.

Because skin does change, so our cleansing routine may have to change. The fact that a routine suited you when you were younger, doesn't mean it is necessarily doing you good now.

Washing

Some women use soap and water most of their lives and are perfectly happy with the condition of their skin. But it can be a rather harsh process for older skins, particularly (as usually happens) if it has become drier than ever. If you must use soap make sure it's a mild one, such as baby soap, and that it doesn't contain any perfume. Perfume can irritate the skin, making it red and blotchy. Vigorous washing can also remove moisture from the skin. As we lose moisture anyway as we get older it makes sense to avoid anything that will

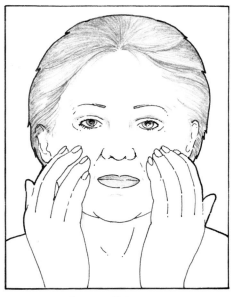

Apply creams and lotions with your fingertips

aggravate the condition.

Always rinse thoroughly with lots of warm water until every trace of soap has gone. Pat, not rub, it dry with a soft towel.

The alternative to soap, and something that gives you the same feeling of satisfaction, is a non-perfumed cleansing bar. It lathers like soap, does a good job of cleaning the skin, and you rinse it off in the same way with lots of water. It is kinder to the skin and leaves it soft and smooth without removing any of the skin's oils.

Soap and cleansing bars are efficient at removing dirt, but are not so effective on make-up. A rinseable cleanser is better. It is also lathered onto the face and washed off, like soap or soap-substitute, but will also remove make-up as efficiently as cleansing cream or lotion.

Cleansing creams and lotions

These do a good job of removing all traces of make-up and grime. They are also good because they clean the skin without drying it. Apply the cream or lotion with your fingers, and tissue off, or use a dampened cottonwool pad to remove. Stroke upwards as you remove

25

the cream, so that you do not pull the skin unnecessarily. Lotions slide on and off more easily than the heavier creams, which means that you are less likely to pull the skin when using them. But many women neglect to clean *the cleanser* off adequately. You must take extra care not to leave surplus cream on the skin. It is as bad as leaving dirt or make-up on.

Removing eye make-up

If your mascara is waterproof, it is difficult to remove with ordinary cleansing cream, and certainly not with warm water. You will need a special eye make-up remover. These can be harsh on the sensitive skin around your eyes. The best ones are 'oil-free' – as they least often cause an allergic reaction. Oil-based eye make-up remover may also make your eyes red and blurry if it runs into them.

If all eye make-up removers irritate your eyes, then you should choose a mascara that is not waterproof. This will wash off in the normal way, or can be removed with your ordinary cleanser.

Whichever eye make-up remover you choose, use a tissue to apply it, preferably dampened first, so you don't put too much remover on the pad. Don't use cotton wool, as minute bits of fluff get caught on your lashes and work their way into your eyes.

Toning

Toning is part of the cleansing process, and shouldn't be left out. It's most important contribution is that it makes sure that every particle of cream (as well as dirt) is removed. Many women leave this stage out, which is one of the reasons they may find their skin has a dull, rather heavy look, instead of a fresh bright appearance.

The easiest method of toning is rinsing with water. If you have switched to creams from soap and water, and miss the feeling of water on your face, you will be pleased to do this. Water tones without drying and is never too strong for your skin.

Alternatively, you can finish off with a commercial toner. These vary considerably, from being very astringent to mild. The astringents are only suitable for oily skins which very few of us still have when we are older. Stick to tonics and fresheners – these contain little or no alcohol, which dries the skin. If you like the idea of a toner, but find it too drying, you can mix a bought one with water to make the strength that suits your skin, or sprinkle it on to a cotton-wool pad that you have already dampened with water.

MOISTURIZING

This is the most important part of your skincare routine. It is moisture-loss that allows wrinkles to form, or become more deeply etched. To stop this happening you must apply a barrier cream, or moisturizer. I always think of a moisturizer as the skin's double-glazing because it protects both sides of the skin – it prevents the moisture being lost and at the same time stops the skin from being battered by the elements outside.

We lose moisture more rapidly when the weather is hot, or when our skin is exposed to cold, dry, windy weather. Moisture-loss also speeds up in centrally-heated or air-conditioned rooms, and when we get hot from cooking. Leaving water to dry on the face, without a protective layer of cream is also dehydrating.

Moisturizers slow up this process of moisture-loss.

Always apply your moisturizing cream straight after cleansing; this will help to prevent the moisture from escaping. If you apply the cream on a slightly damp skin it is even better.

There are many different kinds of products on the market. The best ones for older skins are those formulated for dry skins. These have the right proportion of oil to water for us.

The thicker the cream or lotion, the better it will prevent water loss. I always use the heaviest cream I can get, both for day and night use.

Massage the cream gently into your skin, working upwards, rather than pulling the skin downwards. Leave the cream to sink into your skin for five minutes, and then blot off the excess. That way, however heavy the cream is, it will not leave your skin feeling greasy.

If you find heavy creams too greasy for you, then try a lighter lotion. But you should be aware that the lighter cream does not 'sink' into your skin, it simply evaporates quickly because it contains more water than oil. A heavier cream does a better job of keeping the moisture sealed in. You should, anyway, use a rich cream at night.

Night care

At night, after cleansing, put some rich night cream onto the palm of your hand to warm it through, then gently smooth it over your face. Don't tug it on, but pat gently into the face. Be very careful around your eyes. This is a most sensitive area as the skin is thinner and drier and has little supporting tissue or fat to keep it plump, so pat the cream on gently, never rub it in. You shouldn't need special eyecreams, just take extra care. After five minutes, wipe off any surplus.

Some women find, however, that even when they apply the night cream very carefully they wake up with puffy eyes in the morning. If the cream is at fault, there are three main possibilities. One is that it really *is* too rich for your eye area, in which case you should choose a separate eye cream. Another is that you could be allergic to lanolin, which is an ingredient in many creams. Try one without lanolin – you can get a small size first to test if it suits you and if it makes any difference. The last reason is that you may be leaving too much cream on your face. Any that is not absorbed after five minutes is not going to go on doing your skin good, as some women hope.

As far as choosing moisturizers and nightcreams go, I cannot emphasize enough that it is not what you spend that counts, it is using them with regularity. An expensive cream does *not* do your skin more good than a cheaper brand.

EXFOLIATING

If you know anything about home decorating you'll know that you don't get the best finish unless you fully prepare the surface. It is the same with your skin.

The surface of your skin – the part you see – is composed of dead cells. As the years go by the skin is less efficient at shedding them, which means it can't perform as well as it should. A build up of old cells gives a dull look to your complexion; it is fresher and brighter when they are removed.

So once or twice a week you should exfoliate, that is slough off the dead cells that lie on the surface of the skin. I use a Buf-Puf – a small abrasive sponge which can be bought in the chemists. The one I use is the least abrasive. I lather it with a soap-free cleansing bar and rub my skin with small, light circular movements. I moisturize lavishly immediately afterwards, and find that my skin is particularly receptive after this treatment – with most of the cream being absorbed.

Sometimes I make an abrasive cream instead, mixing half a teaspoon of salt to a teaspoon of cream or olive oil which I massage into the skin in the same way, and then rinse off thoroughly with warm water and the cleansing bar. Always work very gently over broken veins or where the skin is very dry, and smooth in a nourishing cream afterwards.

FACE MASKS

A face mask can be the quick revitalizing tonic your skin needs when it's looking tired and lifeless. It performs very much the same function as the exfoliating techniques, but feels more luxurious and special. And if you lie down at the time for fifteen minutes, perhaps with slices of cold cucumber placed over your eyelids, the rest is pleasant and beneficial. During the early days of the war when my mother and I sat in the air-raid shelter at the bottom of our garden, we'd often put on a face mask for something to do. 'If we have to go, we might as well go looking beautiful,' my mother used to say, and I always took her quite seriously.

Masks don't work miracles, but they do stimulate the circulation, and leave the skin looking smoother and fresher. Don't use one just before going out, or even on the day of a special occasion. The skin is quite pink for about an hour afterwards and needs time to settle down; sometimes it also brings impurities to the surface, and you don't want a spot when you are hoping to look your best.

Be careful which mask you choose. Because skin is drier now, you should avoid any mask that hardens on the skin, as they absorb some of the skin's natural oils.

I used to use mud masks frequently, the kind that, as they dry, feel as if the face is being squeezed into a tight ball. I thought that powerful action was doing my face the world of good. On the contrary, it did more harm than good to my already dry, sensitive skin. My face would glow like a beacon, with danger lights flashing from the broken veins. Dry skins need soft cream masks, which nourish rather than tone. The ones to go for contain natural ingredients like egg, vegetable oils, honey, avocado and fruits and vegetables. They work gently: cleaning the skin deeply and increasing the flow of blood to the skin's surface, they also make the skin feel smoother and plumper afterwards.

If you've got a sturdy skin, you could try the brush-on, scrub-off masks that set like a skin on the face and which you later peel off. They're the least messy of all the masks but they also can be a bit drying.

MIRACLE CREAMS

I'm not going to suggest you buy the wonderful-sounding creams and masks you read about that contain secret ingredients – or special vitamins, collagen,

---

LOOKING GOOD HINTS

● Don't put tinted powder over your foundation cream. It will highlight every line and give your face an unnatural colour.

● Put a light dusting of blusher round the jawline if you have a double chin – but blend it in with the brush very well, or you may leave a tide mark.

● Beware of lipstick on your teeth, it ruins the prettiest smile! This usually happens when you don't blot your lipstick, and leave it 'jammy'. Always check your teeth ten minutes after applying your make-up, and always before you leave the house.

● Put a touch of gloss on your cheek bone. It emphasizes the curve more naturally than a powder highlighter.

● Dark matt lipstick makes the mouth look hard. Pale colours with a slight shine make the lips look fuller.

● If you want to 'set' your make-up so that it lasts the whole day or evening, copy beautician Claire Kitchen's method. She gets in the bath after she's put on her full make-up. She says the steam not only sets her make-up, but gives her skin a lasting glow.

● Using a lip protector like Chapstick or Blistese stimulates the skin on the lips, gives them definition and makes them appear plumper.

● Strong eyebrows are an asset, but if they are bushy and refuse to lie flat, you can trim them carefully with small, sharp scissors. Smooth them down afterwards with Vaseline.

● If you are long-sighted your

hormones, turtle oil or whatever – that are supposed to be miraculously rejuvenating. Unfortunately, there is no evidence that any of them make much difference at all. Your skin will do just as well with the ingredients that are used in cheaper products.

But I must admit that I've always been a sucker for the extravagant claims made by the cosmetic houses and I succumb every so often to some new product and give it a try. Psychologically, they always give me a boost. I can hardly wait to get home so I can try out a new cream or make-up. I'm sure I look better for a while, just because I think I'm going to! It happens to be my pet extravagance and I find it great fun rather than a serious business.

However, I've rarely bought a second jar of any of them, which either means that they did nothing for me or that I didn't give them a fair trial. I'm usually disappointed in the end, because my expectations were raised too high by the promises.

There is one quite new kind of cream, though, which I strongly recommend – I've lost count of the number of jars that I have bought. It is a moisturizer with a built-in sunscreen. A number of different cosmetic manufacturers make them, and I use Martha Hill's own brand. I wish these had been obtainable years ago. I'm sure I wouldn't have half as many brown spots on my hands if I'd protected them with it then as I do now.

I never use anything else when I leave the house. Ordinary bright dayight, as well as sunshine, has harmful rays, and so I use a sun-block moisturizer on my face and hands the whole year round, not just in the summer. As I am a great walker, I now feel quite relaxed when I'm out in the open.

If it's bitterly cold and windy, I also put a thin layer of Vaseline on first. It remains on the surface of the skin, giving it really good protection. You can put a light layer of foundation on top to take off the shin if you like, or dust over it lightly with translucent powder.

THE SKIN'S ENEMY

Unfortunately, the one thing most of us love so much – basking in the sun – is very bad for our skins. My mother's generation tended to have good complexions all their lives, and that was partly because they didn't have the time or opportunity to loll about in the

---

glasses will magnify your eyes, so your normal eye make-up should be sufficient. But if you are short-sighted, your glasses will make your eyes appear smaller, so you will need to accentuate them with a slightly stronger shade of eye-shadow, and you should use an eye-liner. Mascara should be thicker, and applied to the bottom lashes as well. If your frames are a distinctive colour, such as green or blue, it looks attractive to introduce this colour into your eye shadow.

● If you are concerned about the lines and shadows around your eyes, do as Lotte Berk does, and wear large, tinted glasses. You can have your prescription lenses tinted. 'They're intriguing and dramatic,' says Lotte, who wears them all the time, 'and it keeps people guessing.'

● If you feel, and look, rather wan and pale, a touch of blusher on your forehead and chin, as well as on your cheekbones, will give a warmer look.

● Claire Kitchen's recipe for stopping make-up 'disappearing' is to use an under-base from Guerlain (pre-maquillage). Claire found this the only way to keep her make-up looking fresh under hot TV lights and says that it is also good in hot weather and for hot flushes.

● An instant beautifier is to smile – it's the most effective and natural face-lift.

● Accentuate your most attractive feature – that is far more effective than playing down a feature that you don't like.

● Don't put shine where you have wrinkles, or it will highlight them. Put it where the skin is smoothest, such as over the cheekbones.

sun. The famous English peaches-and-cream complexion has a lot to do with our climate. Even in my mother's day a woman who had lived abroad for years in a hot climate – perhaps as the wife of a serving soldier – was always recognizable by her parched, lined skin. Shady hats and a dab of cream weren't sufficient to protect them from the ravages of the sun.

Nowadays we know what can happen when we rush off on long hot holidays abroad. The sun tan that makes you look wonderful while it lasts also damages the deeper layers of skin where the new skin is made. That means you pay years later with more lines than you should have, or worse: doctors have linked skin-cancer with over-enthusiastic sunbathing.

One of my ex-models looked after her skin scrupulously all her life, using every single cream she could, and the most expensive sort. But nowadays her skin looks old before its time. The trouble was that she would dash off to the sun whenever she had the chance in between modelling jobs. She had the most fantastic suntan the whole year round and we were green with envy in the office. Her older sister, who never bothered much with skincare, and never had the looks to be a model, now looks younger than she does.

Many women may not have been sunworshippers when they were younger, but find that they now have the opportunity, time and money to spend on themselves without feeling guilty. This often means more and more holidays in the sun. It's a wonderful tonic, getting away from it all, particularly during the winter months when it cuts down the waiting time for spring.

But although the sun is a marvellous revitalizer, relaxing and stimulating at the same time, you must still bear in mind that in large doses it is destructive. You may think a few extra wrinkles is a small price to pay for hours stretched out lazily on a beach, and that it doesn't matter as long as you've got a tan. But just look around you on the beach. The brownest of the older bodies have skin like well-worn leather, with the surface skin so tough that a moisturizing cream does no more than slither off the top. It looks even worse once you're back home.

Attitudes have changed regarding suntans. It's no longer considered the most attractive thing to burn yourself to a dark brown. On fair skins, the most flattering colour is golden brown and too dark a tan is thought as passé as too heavy make-up.

It's so easy to protect yourself that it's only common sense to do so.

How to enjoy the sun without ill-effects

Ann Melrose, that remarkable yachtswoman who at sixty-three was making plans to compete in an Atlantic boat race, gave me some very good tips when I saw her recently. Despite her many years of sailing and of being exposed to all extremes of weather, she has beautiful skin, scarcely a trace of a line even around her eyes and shining, honey-coloured hair.

'What's your secret?' I asked.

'Well, believe it or not,' she said, 'At one time I daren't expose a single part of myself to the sun. Because I'm basically a redhead, I have the worst possible skin for burning. Whenever I went sailing I was literally wrapped up from top to toe, including my face. It was uncomfortable as well as restricting, as you can imagine. When good sun barrier creams came out I started using them of course, but the big discovery – something that quite honestly changed my life – was Ro-A-Vit. It is vitamin A, and I take a course of twenty-one pills twice a year, a month or so before exposing myself to the sun. Actually, I take half before I go and the other half when I arrive at my destination. I can now sunbathe like anyone else, and I never burn. I quickly develop a light suntan, and with the barrier cream, my skin remains good.'

It certainly does. In the cold winter light it had the lightest tan, and was glowing and healthy. Before barrier creams were available she used Nivea and Ponds cold cream all the time, never exposing her naked skin to the weather.

You should, of course, ask your doctor before prescribing yourself a similar course of vitamin A pills.

These are my own guidelines for enjoying the sun:

● Protect yourself with a sunscreen with the highest protection factor. Screens are usually numbered from 2 to 9, and the higher the number, the greater the protection. Use whenever you are in bright sunlight and reapply after you've been swimming. Even 'total sun blocks' allow some tanning rays through, and give you a light tan. I use a total sun block on my face, and an ordinary high-protection factor sun cream on the rest of my body.

● Start slowly. Fair skins should not sunbathe for longer than thirty minutes on the first day: a little longer for darker skins. Work up to longer stretches by a quarter of an hour each day.

● Keep out of the midday sun. It's the hottest and most damaging time. I like to go onto the beach in the early morning, when there are usually fewer people around anyway, or in the mid-afternoon. Rent a sunshade, counting it as an essential part of your holiday expenses.

● Drink plenty of water, because otherwise you can become dehydrated, which will make you feel ill. If you're uneasy about the tap variety, buy sparkling or plain bottled mineral water.

● Protect your eyes. That sensitive skin area will suffer most from a sun tan. When I was working in Majorca the local paper advised on skin care, not just for the tourists but for all-year-round residents. The beauty writer suggested wearing plastic eye shades when lying on the beach or sitting .on the

Ann Melrose, yachtswoman, born in 1923. No photograph can do justice to Ann's glowing, smooth complexion and shining gold-tipped hair. I was filled with admiration when I met her, not just because of her positive attitude to life.

'The more you do, the more it generates excitement' she told me. 'I have a great excitement for life and I feel I hardly have time to do all the things I want to do. I am not afraid of the risks I take when I sail the Atlantic. I have faith in God – and it brings out the fighting spirit in me!'

balcony. I prefer to wear a good pair of sunglasses all the time when the weather is sunny. It means slightly paler patches of skin around my eyes compared with the rest of my face, but I cover this up with a tinted make-up. If you wear glasses all the time, it's worth getting tinted prescription lenses. Photosensitive lenses — the kind that lighten and darken according to the intensity of light — are marvellous because you don't have to keep taking them on and off when the light changes. Recent research shows that sunglasses are also a prevention against cataracts.

One excellent tip: if you find, like me, that your glasses slide around on your nose once you start to perspire, it probably drives you mad. I dampen my finger with a good anti-perspirant and rub it over my nose in the morning, and I find the effect lasts almost all day.

● Use a roll-on deodorant (deodorants make you smell nicer, but don't actually stop you perspiring). A roll-on is easier to carry around than a spray. Don't put it on immediately after a bath or when you are perspiring as it will be quickly absorbed by the open pores. When I'm very hot I put a cold compress, consisting of a flannel wrapped round ice, under my arms and pat myself dry before applying a deodorant.

● To stop perspiration completely, you need to use an anti-perspirant. I use one as little as possible, as I prefer the gentler action of a deodorant. I believe that you only need to use an anti-perspirant when you are fully dressed, to prevent the underarms of your clothes getting spoilt. In light summer clothes this is rarely a problem.

● Keep your head and the back of your neck covered. Hair needs as much protection as skin to prevent the natural oils from drying out. If it's permed or coloured the strong light will fade the colour and over-dry the perm. Keep it covered with a hat or scarf. Always rinse your hair as soon as possible after swimming in the sea or a pool as salt and chemicals are damaging. Before shampooing your hair rub in a little warmed olive oil then wrap it in a warm towel for about half an hour before shampooing. It's an excellent reviver for sun-dried hair.

● Apply lashings of after-sun cream after sunbathing. Put oil in your bath, too — but be very careful about slipping. If there isn't an anti-slip mat, lay a small hand towel in the bath. Don't soak for more than ten minutes. If you prefer to shower, reapply body cream afterwards.

● Obviously, if you get badly sun-

EVENING GLAMOUR TRICKS

Choose one or two of these hints to give your evening look an extra sparkle.

● A touch of gold highlighter to the centre of the eyelids brightens the eyes.

● Silver glitter can be dabbed on the ear lobes instead of ear-

rings. Or, if you are grey, it can be brushed lightly round the hairline making a pretty frame for the face. Or the smallest touch can be placed in the hollow of the neck.

● If your lower lip is thin, a touch of dark pencil in the centre will make it appear fuller.

● Irridescent powder brushed lightly on the cheekbone will

highlight the shape of your face.

● The tiniest triangle of white highlighter, or pale concealer stick in a triangle in the corner of the eyes will give the whites of your eyes a fresh look.

● White kohl pencil applied along the rim of the lower lashes opens up the eyes. Most actresses of all ages use this simple trick to get a wide-eyed look.

burnt you should see a doctor. But if you have stayed out in the sun too long inadvertently and are slightly burnt, you can usually deal with it yourself:

— Cool the skin with calamine lotion

— Make cold compresses with ice cubes wrapped in a cloth

— Take aspirin or paracetamol for pain relief

— Apply a mixture of half vinegar/ half water to the affected part

● If you've got patches of skin with no pigmentation (white patches) or skin with over-pigmentation (brown patches) you should avoid the sun as much as possible, as these areas will be emphasized by a tan. Use a total sun-block on any skin that is exposed, and cover up when possible. Fine cotton dresses or shirts with full-length sleeves are useful. I always take at least one away with me if I'm going to a hot country to prevent my arms and shoulders from burning when I'm out sight-seeing. The unwaisted ones are the coolest and they make excellent cover-ups for the beach as well.

● If you want a tan without the risk of sun-bathing, then you can fake it. I prefer not to use the 'fake tans' that take a couple of hours or so to develop and last for days, as it is hard to control the strength or evenness of the colour. I usually use a waterproof cream make-up in a suntan shade. I use it on my bare legs and lightly on my face once a natural tan has started. Like any make-up, it has to be taken off at the end of the day, but it has a very natural look, and you can get precisely the shade you prefer.

CARE OF THE SKIN IN WINTER

Looking after skin in the sun is a fairly new preoccupation for most of us. But cold weather is another matter. Biting winds, temperatures hovering around freezing for long stretches of time,

these are things we're very familiar with, and they play havoc with our skin if we're not careful. Central heating has added to our problems. Coming in out of the cold makes the face turn bright red. I cup my face in my hands to warm it a little before going inside, which helps, and is kinder to broken veins which tend to flare up in extremes of temperature.

Here are some tips to help you cope with the winter months:

● Unless you have no alternative, don't walk headlong into the wind. It may feel wonderful but it is ruinous to the skin. If you have no choice, then cover as much of your face as you can with a scarf.

● Put a fine film of Vaseline, olive oil, or baby oil (or whatever oil you have in the kitchen) on your skin and lips before applying your normal moisturizer and make-up.

● If your skin feels drier and more taut than usual, then your skincare routine could be at fault. If you normally wash with soap, avoid it at this time. It is even more drying in the winter. Use cleansing cream, or a soap-less cleansing block. Use a specially rich night cream at night, leave it on for five minutes and then blot off any surplus as usual.

● If you have central heating, place bowls of water in the room to prevent the air getting dry. Or buy the humidifiers that latch over the radiators.

● Give your hands and neck the same protection as your face. Wear gloves and keep your neck covered with a scarf when you go out.

● Don't lick your lips when out in the cold as it causes them to crack. Carry a lip salve or Vaseline with you so you can apply it whenever they feel dry.

● Remember that make-up actually protects your skin in bad weather, as well as giving it a much smoother, even-looking texture.

MAKE-UP

A little bit of powder,
A little bit of paint,
Makes a lady pretty,
When she really ain't.

My mother used to sing this to me when I was a child as she rubbed Ponds cold cream into her face, following it with a quick rub of powder cream and finishing off with a dab of lipstick. Hardly an elaborate beauty routine but one she carried out religiously each day after she'd washed and tidied herself up for the evening.

For many years, unless you were an actress or model, make-up was not very much more complicated than this. But in the 1950s the craze was for heavy Pan-Stik, thick layers of powder and hard, dark lipstick. There was little choice in make-up, but what you wore was so heavy that everyone knew you had it on. I remember, around that time, when I arranged to have lunch with a friend I hadn't seen since the war. We'd been in the A.T.S. together as drivers, and in the meantime we'd both married and had children. I was working as a model and was a bit worried about meeting her with all my make-up on, so I managed to wipe a good deal of it off before I got to the restaurant. I was afraid she might mind if I looked too glamorous! Imagine my embarrassment when her husband, whom I also knew, gave one horrified look at me and said, 'Good God! You look like the back row of the chorus!'

From the point of view of natural looks, things went from bad to worse in the 60s and 70s, the time of 'swinging London'. Many of my friends shunned make-up altogether because it was so artificial and complicated. There became less of a gap between the theatrical and the ordinary. Heavy false eyelashes, fluorescent eyeshadows, thick black eyeliners were all part of what you wore. Round faces, long faces, thin ones, fat ones had their shading and rouging instuctions to help make them fit into the conventional idea of beauty — no wonder so many women thought it better to use nothing at all than look ridiculous.

The effect was ageing, unquestionably. The youngest teenager looked as if she was well into her 20s.

More recently a timeless fashion for natural looks has emerged, alongside other more bizarre looks, such as punk. It is a good time to be an older woman as far as make-up is concerned. Discreet make-up is very flattering: just enough to enhance the features and make the skin glow. There are some excellent cosmetics around to help you achieve this, and I will tell you how to do it. Remember, even if you are pleased with the way you do your make-up, if you have been putting it on the same way for a few years it is probably time for a change. Make-up methods and colours date after a while, and if you continue to use the same products and colours you will 'place' yourself in a particular era. I ran across one of my top models from the 1960s the other day, and I noticed that she still had that highly-plucked look about her eyebrows, and wore heavy eyeliner. She was only in her early 40s, but she hadn't kept in touch and looked very dated.

The Essentials

If you want to look your best, you can't get away with just a little dab of lipstick, and a little dab of powder. As with clothes, you don't need a vast selection, but what you have must be right. I'll give you a list of the minimum of essentials, to which you can add your own favourites. On the whole, I don't favour one kind of make-up over another. Many of the cheaper ranges are made by cosmetic houses in exactly

Left: Pauline Yates, who is presently in the American TV series Hold the Dream *succeeds in looking so incredibly young (she's just had her fiftieth birthday) because she goes in for the natural, casual look. Her short hair is unstructured and the cleverly applied make-up appears not to be there at all. We may need more make-up as we get older, but the secret is not to let it show.*

Above: A well made-up face and (below), a face that has been too heavily made-up

(but not direct sunlight), or bright artificial light (though not fluorescent light, as it drains colour). You also need a large magnifying mirror, one of the necessary evils, to my mind. It's an absolute must for checking that your make-up is applied perfectly. It is *not* for scrutinizing wrinkles, blotches, broken veins or any other unlikables. If they can't be seen by the naked eye, why go searching for them? As Martha Hill, the incredible-looking seventy-five year old boss of her own beauty company says, 'Nobody stares into your face looking for wrinkles. And nobody sees a face as huge as the one that stares back at you from a magnifying mirror'. She also advises those who can't see clearly without their glasses not to use eye make-up at all. 'It's the one area,' she says, 'where you must see what you're doing otherwise you'll end up looking a mess.' I can't see clearly without my glasses but I *can* see with a magnifying mirror – and if *you* can, then you should be all right with eye make-up too.

I won't tell you how to *alter* the shape of your face with blushers and shaders – quite frankly, it never works. But they do give warmth and definition to your features. It amazes me how many beauty books and magazines tell you how you can disguise just about every feature of a perfectly normal face. Which doesn't mean there aren't tricks worth learning that can *improve* the way you look.

Tools for the job
- Magnifying mirror.
- One large brush for powder.
- Two eye brushes for eye shadow. One straight-edged, full-bristled one, and another small, very thin brush for outlining.
- One brush for rouge or blusher.
- One eyelash brush/comb.
- One lipstick brush (this should have short, hard bristles, cut across diagonally in a straight line so that you get a clean line when you

the same way as the expensive ranges. The individual ingredients used in make-up are not expensive, it is the packaging and advertizing that sends the prices up, so most of the make-up I buy is in the lower price range. Usually, though, the range of colours is more varied in the more expensive ranges, so if you are looking for a particular shade you may have to pay more.

The single most important thing when putting on make-up is to see yourself clearly. That means you need excellent light, either strong daylight

are putting on lipstick).
- One pencil sharpener (choose a cosmetic one, as ordinary pencil sharpeners won't take the fat cosmetic pencils).
- Eyebrow tweezers.

Optional
- Eyelash curlers — if like me, you've always yearned for sweeping lashes.
- Swansdown powder puff as an alternative to a brush.
- Make-up sponge.

The basic cosmetics

Foundation
This is the basis of all successful make-up. It protects the skin and evens out the skin tones, covers blemishes and gives a better colour and texture.

Liquid foundation is the easiest to apply, it is light in texture and practically invisible on the face so it is perfect if you want the very lightest covering.

If you need something heavier, to cover broken veins, dark circles under the eyes, or slight scarring, then a solid foundation in stick form, such as Pan-Stik, gives denser cover. I use this on the broken veins on my cheeks, and find it is the only make-up that covers them well. It mustn't be applied thickly. Two thin layers are better than one thick one: you can get the very lightest effect by applying it thinly, with a dampened sponge or with slightly damp fingers. However, if your skin

has large open pores, or is pitted in any way, then it will be too heavy for you.

If you have a high colour or get easily flushed you can buy a green under-base from Boots which will tone down the red.

Foundation should be as near your own skin colour as possible. You need two shades — a lighter one in the winter and a darker one as the sun changes your skin tone. The beige colours, either light or medium, are usually suitable for most skins. Keep away from anything with a pink or orange tint.

I find it's easiest to use the fingers when applying foundation. Unless you're quite experienced you can put on far too much with a sponge, but with your fingers you can work it more easily into the difficult areas around the nose and mouth.

Take your time when applying foundation. It must be smoothly blended-in right up to your hairline, and under your chin, so that there are no 'edges' where it suddenly stops.

Powder
You need a box of colourless, translucent loose powder in the finest texture. Don't buy anything with colour in it. It invariably darkens on the skin and gives that powdered look that isn't flattering, particularly in the bright sunlight.

Powder is used to 'set' the foundation, and shouldn't be noticeable in itself.

Dust the powder on with a large brush or fluffy powder puff. Don't rub or pat it into the skin. Brush your face, with downward strokes after applying, so that you take off any excess.

Never use solid, compressed powders. They can go patchy on the skin and tend to darken. They are often recommended for touching up make-up, but I don't advise them. If you need to powder while you are out, take your loose powder with you.

Blushers or Rouge

Cream rouge is best. It's more natural and has a glow rather than the rather flat, artificial look that powder rouge can give. It is always applied under powder, unlike powder blushers which are put on top. Choose muted shades with brown or burgundy overtones. They sound rather dark but are surprisingly good and much better than the pinks, oranges or cyclamen. Powder blusher is useful for 'touching up' while you are out, though.

Blemish stick

This is for covering red veins, dark shadows and other blemishes. Choose a natural colour. Put it on with your fingers, before using a foundation.

Lipstick base

I use a lip base cream, Lip-Fix, which I find helps the lipstick to stay put and provides a nice, smooth base. If your lips have lost definition, the cream also helps to redefine them.

Lipsticks

It's useful to have a selection of colours and as the inexpensive ones are excellent you can buy three for the price of a dearer one. Don't choose over-bright shades such as clear reds or those with purple tones — muted pinks, burgundies and browny shades of red are much more flattering. Lipstick often turns a bluish tone on the mouth, so test it first on the pad of a finger. If it turns bluish after five or ten minutes, it will do the same on your mouth. Lipstick shouldn't be too glossy; go for the translucent brands, which give a shine without being 'jammy'. Beware of putting lipgloss over lipstick as it causes the colour to smudge.

The longest lasting lip colour is applied with a brush. Like this, you can work the lipstick well into the lines of the lips. It is worth the little extra time spent.

Lipstick pencil

A lipstick pencil in rosy-beige is the best buy. This is close to the natural colour of the mouth. The pencil prevents the lipstick from creeping into the tiny lines above the mouth, and defines the natural shape of your lips. Don't use a lipstick pencil to change the shape. It looks very artificial.

Eyebrow pencil

You need a pencil the same colour as your eyebrows. Don't draw one heavy arc, but make short, feathery strokes that look like hairs that blend in with your own eyebrows.

Eye shadows

Powders are best. Creams are inclined to get stuck in the creases, run into lines and look less natural than powder. You want a shadow — not a blob of colour. The best shades for most eyes are browny green, blue/grey and taupe, but if you buy a mixed palette of colours you can experiment with them; make-up artists mix colours on the back of their hands to get the exact shade they want.

Practise using different colours. Try out new colours before a special occasion, so you can see whether they suit you.

Eye pencils

I'm inclined to avoid these for everyday use as they can drag the skin around the eyes, and often give a crinkly, rather than a smooth line. If you also like to use them as liners or shadows, bear these things in mind: test the pencil on the pouch of skin between thumb and forefinger. If the skin drags at all, so will the skin round your eyes; the pencil should glide across. A very soft pencil is also less stable than a powder shadow or line, so after using, powder over with your normal face powder to set it. Hastily applied pencil lines can look crude. Work them in with an eyeshadow brush.

Mascara

Mascara is essential if you are using eye shadow or eye liner, otherwise the eyes have a strange, unfinished look. Famous make-up artist Clayton Howard, an absolute wizard with eyes, told me, when we were doing a show together, that I ought to wear mascara on the lower lashes as well as it makes the eyes look larger. I'd always thought it made the eyes look hard and over made-up, and I was agreeably surprised to see how effective it was. It has to be done carefully so there are no smudges. Use an eyelash brush to separate the lashes afterwards, so they don't stick together.

I find wand mascaras are the easiest to handle. Avoid those with pieces of filament added to make your lashes thicker. They usually end up on your face. If you want thicker eyelashes, try a model's trick that we used in the 50s. Apply one layer of mascara, and before it is quite dry, powder over with face powder. Then put mascara on again. The tiny fragments of powder thicken the lashes more naturally than the hairy filaments.

Martha Hill, who has her own unique ideas on how to apply make-up, tells me she never uses brushes of any description — not even mascara brushes. She demonstrated to me how she advises her customers to put on her cream mascara. She put a dab of mascara on her little finger, then, resting the thumb on the opposite temple to the eye to be made-up, brushed the lashes with her little finger. 'You can feel what you're doing,' she said, 'and you don't have any messy brushes or stuck together eyelashes!'

Avoid black macara. It is too harsh and unkind, brown is much kinder and just as effective. All bright-coloured mascara is taboo!

Step-by-step to the basic face

This is what I think of as a good 'all-purpose' basic make-up. It is a natural look that is right for every occasion except a glamorous night out, and will suit you whatever your colouring. You can vary the colours to make your look more individual, but you will find that these discreet shades look surprisingly different on everyone.

1. Apply your moisturizer, leave for a few minutes until it is absorbed, and then pat off any excess.

2. Tip a little foundation into your hand if you are using liquid, and gently smooth it on your face with your fingers. Blend it under your chin, but don't carry it down your neck or your clothes will get marked. That is why it is important to choose a colour that matches your skin tone. If you have the right shade there will be no tell-tale mark.

Clean excess make-up from your hairline with cotton wool, and also at the side of your nose. Be careful not to use too much. You only need the lightest covering. Be gentle around the eyes, patting it in. Carry the cream over your eyelids and mouth.

If you have any blemishes you wish to cover, pat over lightly with a little blemish cream on your finger, working the colour in carefully so there's no hard line.

If you have a high colour use a green underbase before your foundation, patting it over the affected areas. It's not as gruesome as it sounds! Provided you don't use too much and smooth it in

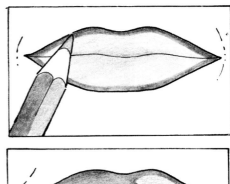

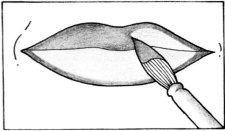

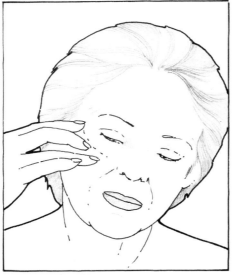

Right: Feel for your cheekbones, and apply rouge along the bone. Far right: correct method of applying lipstick

well, it doesn't give your skin a greeny tinge – but it does counteract the red, which is a great confidence booster if you turn bright pink after the first glass of wine.

3. Feel for your cheekbones, and place tiny dots of cream rouge along the bone from the centre of your cheek to the outer eye. Smooth it in so there is no edge of colour. This will highlight your cheekbone and give definition and 'lift' to your face. Don't put rouge too close to the nose as it draws the face forward in an ageing way. If you place it too low, the cheeks appear to be sunken.

4. Dust translucent powder generously all over your face, including your lashes, and then lightly brush off the excess. Brush downwards, so that you smooth down the soft hairs on your face.

5. At this stage, contrary to the usual method, I like to put on lipstick. The all-over powdered look, with eyes and mouth 'blotted' out can be rather off-putting! It also makes it much easier to see how much eye make-up is needed to balance the face. Place a tissue be-

tween your lips, and 'bite' down with your lips to remove any surplus foundation.

6. Now very carefully define the outline of your lips with a well-sharpened lipstick pencil – you will find that you have a natural line to follow. This takes a steady hand and a bit of practise but it's well worth persevering to get a good clean line which should last all day. Don't try to draw the line in one continuous movement. Steady your elbow on the table and draw a line from one point of your 'cupid's bow' to the corner of your mouth. Do the same the other side. After this, fill in the curve of the bow. Finally, draw in the line of your underlip.

7. Use a lipbrush to fill in the lipstick, working with the brush to blur the lip line and lipstick. If you prefer to apply the lipstick straight from the case take care not to go over the edges of the line you've pencilled in, working the lipstick inside with your little finger. Blot with a tissue, dust over with a little powder, and apply more lipstick. Then bite on a tissue again to remove the last traces of excess lipstick and you should be all set for the day. Only the very

minimum should come off, and your lipstick won't smudge or 'creep'.

8. Now for your eye make-up — perhaps the most rewarding part of your whole make-up, and the most difficult to apply. Take your time over it, and only put a little shadow on your brush at a time. Too heavy and too dark eye make-up defeats its purpose of making the eyes look brighter, larger and more interesting. Bear in mind that you are aiming for a shadowy effect with no harsh lines. The most effective make-up is the simplest, which you apply in the following stages:

a. with your brush, blend taupe brown powder over your eyelids to your eyebrow.

b. with a darker shade of brown, brush a line of shadow, with your smallest, very slim brush, along the upper lid close to the lashes, to make a shadowy eye-line.

c. with the same darker shade, lightly brush under the lower lashes curving it round the outer corner of the eye to meet the line on the upper lid. Smooth into a soft unbroken shadow with a cotton bud.

(Stand back from the mirror and examine yourself. Your eyes should look larger and more distinctive.)

d. Apply mascara to the upper lashes, lifting — but not stretching — the lid slightly with the finger of your other hand. I always curl my lashes first with an eyelash curler. It's most effective and makes it easier to put on mascara if your lashes are short and straight. Put the very lightest touch on your bottom lashes and then check in the magnifying mirror for smudges. Separate lashes that have stuck together with an eyelash brush. One coat should be sufficient for a natural look.

e. have a good look in your magnifying mirror and remove any splodges with a cotton bud dipped lightly in eye make-up remover.

(For an even more natural look, instead of using a taupe shadow, brush over the entire eye lid with a powder blusher in a rosy pink. Use it very, very lightly, for a healthy glow.)

9. Next, brush your eyebrows in the opposite direction to their natural growth (an old toothbrush is good for this). This will take out any excess powder. If your brows are sparse, then using short feather strokes lightly pencil in the sparse areas. Smooth back into shape with the brush, and brush through again to blend the lines.

If you have no eyebrows, don't be tempted to draw them on to your face. It's far better to disguise the fact by pulling your hair forward in a wave or fringe.

Putting on the glamour at night
Going out somewhere special in the evening calls for a more adventurous make-up if you don't want to look washed out. Artificial light drains colour and vitality from the face. I have a friend who looks wonderful during the day because her skin is good and she uses just a discreet make-up to give her a natural glowing look. But at night when she's all dressed up and wearing her pretty jewellery, instead of looking stunning, she looks washed out.

'I can't stand looking over-made-up,' she once said to me, 'but I know I never look as nice in the evening as I do during the day.' As she loves going out to special functions and she adores the theatre, she really wanted to know what to do about it. I gave her these hints.

Looking good in the evening doesn't mean going over the top. It means adding a little bit more. First you must make up in the kind of light you'll be exposed to. If you are going to a friend's house, her lighting will be much the same as yours – but a vast hall or theatre could have fluorescent or very bright lighting. If you can't duplicate that kind of light, just remember that you'll need more colour on your face. Follow the same routine as for your daytime make-up but add the extra touches that give you glamour.

1. If you tend to flush take precautions before you go out, rather than expect to 'touch up' during the evening with a powder compact, which only builds up a rather blotchy colour.

Carefully pat green corrective cream on the areas of your face and neck that flush easily. Do this on a clean skin, not over a moisturizer, and it will stay on better. Concentrate on special places like broken veins or red patches. Then apply your foundation in the usual way. If you don't have a problem with flushing use the lightest moisturizer only before putting on your foundation.

2. I also like to use an additional under-base for the evening. It looks rather white when it is applied, but it is light-reflective and glows through your usual foundation, to give a fresh, younger look to the skin. A number of cosmetic houses make it. The one I find effective is Clinique's Extra Help.

3. On top, use a foundation in a slightly darker colour than you would normally use (your summer base will do) as it will give your skin the warmth it needs under artificial light. But do blend in the area under your chin particularly well.

4. With your lighter, daytime foundation, pat carefully over any dark shadows under the eyes, and smooth some on the nose-to-mouth lines.

5. Put cream rouge on your cheekbones, from the centre of your cheek to the hairline, but use quite a bit more than you do during the day – in fact you can make it rather obvious-looking, as it tends to disappear during the evening. It not only gives you colour where you want it (which is often quite different from where you flush naturally), but it also defines the shape of your face.

6. Powder in the usual way, brushing off excess afterwards.

7. Cover the whole eye area from lid to brow with a grey/blue or greeny/brown shadow. You have to discover for yourself what suits you best as it's difficult to lay down definite rules about colour.

It's easier to say what shouldn't be used: don't choose anything that is too brightly coloured or that is frosted or shiny, as these show up imperfections.

The easiest way to add colour and sparkle to your eyes is with a thin eye-line of colour. You can use a very soft pencil for this. A silvery green or blue is good with grey hair, for example. A golden amber is fine with brown hair. Draw a line on the upper lid, close to your lashes, making sure the pencil has a sharp point.

Under your eye, echo the colour of your shadow by brushing a thin line of colour round to the outer edge of your eye.

8. Make up your mouth in the usual way. But you can wear a much more glowing colour than usual as the artificial lights will tone it down. However, don't choose a colour that fights with your dress i.e. orange against scarlet, and keep away from colours with a blue or brown tint, as they don't look good under artificial light.

HAIR

If you've got beautiful, manageable hair, thank your lucky stars! You are

Right: I love this picture of Jeanne Moreau, who is now in her fifties, because it shows her vibrant glowing personality. I know her hair is too long and the fringe too heavy (she looks altogether better when she wears it softly piled up on top) but she looks very womanly *and this is an endearing quality.*

Jeanne Moreau is an elegant woman. She knows *how to make the best of herself but she also has the confidence to allow her appearance to fit in with her moods.*

Top: Lotte Berk, the small and intriguing 'Queen of Physical Fitness' was born in 1913. She wears her hair in a sleek bob with a fringe but has chosen not to go grey.

'Grey hair is not for me', she says, 'It doesn't suit my personality. I have it coloured to this glossy reddish brown. I have a great sense of the dramatic which is why I always dress in black and wear huge dark glasses and lots of eye make up. I change the brightness of my lipstick according to my mood. But you know, flirting is what really keeps you young and attractive'.

Martha Hill is a remarkably vivacious woman in her mid-seventies and a wonderful advertisement for her own herbal beauty products. She 'likes to look pretty and fresh rather than elegant.'

She wears her hair in a youthful bob and it suits her perfectly. 'I don't put any colour on it whatsoever,' she says. She doesn't like wearing dark colours. She thinks they are depressing for older women, whereas the pale soft colours have an uplifting effect.

the envy of so many of us whose hair is the bane of our lives.

Many of our problems exist because we have given too much, rather than too little attention to our hair over the years. We've all sat for hours at some time or another under hair dryers that have dried up our hair and scorched the back of our neck mercilessly. I remember in the 60s hardly anyone I knew even shampooed their own hair any more. In the famous salons it was normal to spend the whole morning or afternoon having a shampoo and comb out, and to get one of the top stylists to do it was like making an appointment with royalty. An appointment, I might add, that could cost a small fortune.

I spent over twenty years having a weekly 'do' because in my business it was imperative to look well-groomed, and yet I never found a style or cut that I could cope with successfully myself! I was not unique in that respect. If I learnt anything at all it was that if you have the right kind of hair a clever cut will solve most of your problems. If you have the typical fine English fly-away hair then it will be a continual battle. Even Joan Collins, who looks as if she has got everything right, says she has fine hair which can't take a perm, and which gets limp and greasy very quickly.

My own hair only started to get back into condition when I stopped treating it as if it was indestructible. Gentle, frequent shampooing at home, drying it naturally with my fingers, avoiding any kind of heat or perming treatments and going regularly to my hairdresser for a cut is having obvious results. This way of dealing with hair is now advocated by the top hairdressers. Apart from getting a good cut when we need it, hair has never been so easy to look after at home. This is good news, for whether our hair is our crowning glory or not, we can't look our best if it's a mess, and hair can make or mar the most attractive woman.

Another difficulty is that hair

changes over the years. The colour fades and eventually goes grey. For many woman this has the hidden bonus that grey hair is thicker and more wiry than the original hair. Some women find that their hair has become thinner. Usually, as our hair changes we have to rethink our hairstyles completely — cut, colour and the way we care for it.

Choosing a style

'What's new in hairstyles?' I asked Derek, my local hairdresser, recently. Derek was a Mayfair stylist for years and knew the 60s and 70s scene as well as I did. He often booked my models for hair photography during that time.

'More relaxed, more natural, quieter colours,' he said. He prefers those looks, as I do. This, of course, is good for us, because stiff hairstyles and un-natural colours are ageing.

Hair should *move*. It should have a natural swing to it, not be stiff with lacquer or permed into a tight little frizz. It shouldn't be bleached yellow or dyed harsh black. It rarely looks good tumbling over the shoulders, either, except on the young. If you've always worn your hair long and it's a positive part of your personality it probably only needs a couple of inches trimmed off to reach a length that is elegant.

Wearing your hair up

Putting my hair up has been a life-saver for me. I have very fine hair with no body, so growing it long and twisting it into a chignon has given it more apparent thickness than ever before. It suits me, it gives a lift to my face, and at the same time it's manageable and elegant — something I never thought I would ever achieve.

Of course, not every woman looks good with her hair back off her face, and for some this style can be severe and ageing.

Getting the right cut

Look at the photographs of Martha

Hill and Lotte Berk, both in their 70s, and both wearing a sleek bob with a fringe. The first thing I noticed about them was their youthful, relaxed hairstyles. Martha allows her hair to remain its natural grey without a colour rinse of any kind, and this suits her fragile, clear complexion. Lotte's dark hair is professionally treated with a vegetable rinse to give it a dark auburn gloss, which is in keeping with her own particular personality. They both have an individual style, they look exceptionally good, and they're both breaking the so-called rules.

Most women, though, look better with a lift at the sides and some fullness on top, especially if like me, they've got a flat crown. The casual, curly short cut is easy to look after and looks very good if it's shiny and healthy. However, this style, when it is over-permed can look dry and lifeless.

These are the important things to think about when you are choosing your style:

• Find the best hairdresser that you can. Word of mouth is the best way. Ask other women whose hair you admire where they get their hair done *particularly* if they have the same kind of hair as you.

• Let your hairdresser see your hair at its worst so all its bad points can be noted and taken into account when he cuts and styles it. Ideally you want a style that you can cope with yourself at home.

• If you have found the right hairdresser, trust his judgement. If not, and you are telling him exactly what to do, remember the following points:

— A really short cut that exposes the sides and the back of the neck is hard to wear because it has no softening lines. Hair must be thick and wiry for the best results. Fine hair flops too easily and gives a 'sat on' look.

Right: Deborah Kerr, now in her sixties, wears her thick fair hair back in a chignon in the tradition of classical beauties. Everything about her has a quiet dignity – her make-up, hairstyle and dress, the kind of looks that most English women admire and feel they can aspire to.

Still as slim as ever, Audrey Hepburn has all the grace and style of a ballerina. Her dark hair is swept high up into a coil, and the dramatic earrings are perfect with her long slim neck. She has inborn style. I remember seeing her a few years ago at Rome airport wearing a simple suit in brown with a cream shirt and large pearl earrings. Her court shoes and handbag were also brown, and her skin was lightly tanned. She wore no other colour and the effect was stunning.

— If you have a flat head or fine hair, ask your hairdresser for a light body perm that gives a lift without much curl.

— If your hair is basically curly, but the crown is flat, ask for a gentle perm just on the crown. This will give you the lift only where you need it.

— Round and square faces need a hairstyle with height and quite a bit of fullness.

Thin faces look better with exra width at the sides.

● Ask your hairdresser to show you how to do your own hair at home. If he uses rollers, learn how to put them in the way he does. If he uses a hand·dryer or tongs to set it then practise the technique too. If you find his techniques too difficult, then insist on a wash-and-wear style that you *can* cope with — or your hair will only look at its best after a visit to the hairdresser.

● *Wash-and-Wear*. This kind of style is easiest to cope with and kindest on the hair, as it is not being pulled about or subjected to heat treatments. Find the way your hair falls naturally by combing it back from your forehead when it's wet and then pushing it forward with your hands. It will fall into its natural place and this is the basic line the hairdresser should follow when creating a style for your hair.

Caring for the hair
As your hair changes in texture and colour, so should your hair care routine. Some women who had greasy hair when they were young fail to notice that their hair has changed, and continue looking after it in the same way — then they can't understand why they can't make it look so good anymore.

Nowadays the range of hair-care products is greater than ever before, and there are gentle, effective shampoos and conditioners and setting lotions for every type of hair.

In the days of harsh shampoos it was considered bad to wash your hair more than once a week — and once a day was unheard of! One of my young models had very greasy hair, and when she first came to me she only 'used' her natural hair one day a week — the rest of the time she wore a wig. Her hair looked lank the day after washing, but her mother had told her that washing more than once a week would do it great harm. I told her that she would just have to wash it come what may — I couldn't have her wearing a wig most of the time. Even so, it was considered rather daring that she washed it so often.

Today nothing seems more normal. Extra gentle shampoos clean without stripping the hair of its natural moisture, which means that we can all wash our hair as and when we think it needs it.

Looking after hair has never been so straightforward — particularly if you have an easy-to-maintain style. There are only a few basic rules to bear in mind.

● Choose the correct products for your type of hair. You need to know whether your hair is dry or greasy, or somewhere in between, and what sort of conditioner, if any, you should use.

● The condition of your hair dictates how often you wash it. Obviously, if it needs washing more than once every three or four days, you need a style you can set yourself. If you do wash it frequently, choose one of the very mildest shampoos, and only lather once, whatever the directions say — there won't be very much 'dirt' to wash off.

● If your hair gets very greasy — which is not usual as we get older — and you don't want to spoil your style by washing frequently, then you can use a dry shampoo in between your regular wash.

● Used correctly, a conditioner will give a lovely shine to your hair, but if you use too much, or the wrong kind, it can make your hair lank. Try applying to to the part of your hair that needs it most, such as the ends, rather than enthusiastically rubbing it in all over.

● If your hair is dry and lifeless, give it an oil treatment every couple of weeks. Massage two tablespoons of warm olive oil into your hair and scalp. Tie it up in a hot towel for twenty minutes and then thoroughly shampoo.

● If you find conditioners are too heavy for your fine, flyaway hair, you can try the old fashioned ploy of giving it a final rinse in beer. It will give it body (in fact it is like a mild setting-lotion) and the smell will soon disappear.

● Don't use a hair-dryer any more than is strictly necessary. It robs the hair of natural oils, as do heated rollers and tongs. Instead towel-dry your hair, then bend your head forward and run your fingers through, scrunching it from time to time to give it body.

● Don't over-brush your hair. That two hundred strokes a day routine we grew up with has long been known to be bad for the hair. It can make it greasy and it weakens the hair. Hair must always be treated with care. Don't brush your hair when it's wet as that is when it stretches and breaks more easily.

● If your hair gets tangles, untangle it before washing, starting from the ends and working up towards the roots.

● If you use lacquer – and do keep it

The Duchess of Argyll now in her seventies, has always been a famous beauty and she projects her own very individual style. The hair remains dark, and her skin ivory white, and she is elegant in the time honoured tradition of expensive furs and jewellery. She has sailed past the ever-changing face of fashion establishing her position as an elegant and beautiful woman.

to a minimum – brush it all out at night, otherwise you'll wake up with lank hair.

● Don't always cover your hair with a hat – fresh air is beneficial. But keep it protected against sun and strong winds.

Hair colours

Next to style, the colour of your hair is the most important consideration. It's difficult to decide what to do when it's fading or at the 'pepper-and-salt' stage.

Many women play safe by having their hair tinted back to their original colour. But this is not, in fact, the safe option. Just as your hair has changed colour, so has your skin. Your original dark or blonde hair may not now look right with the colour of your skin. It doesn't mean that you have to leave your hair to go whatever colour it wants, but it does mean choosing a new colour, or streaks of colour, that are complementary.

Elizabeth Taylor is a good example of a woman who finally recognized the truth of this. For years she kept her very dark hair colour, which began to look harsh against her skin – it was ageing, not youthful, as she apparently thought. After her well-publicized, rejuvenated emergence from the Betty Ford clinic I was particularly struck by her appearance. Yes, she was now off alcohol and drugs, yes she had lost weight, and yes, she had had a face lift. But what really made the radical difference as far as I was concerned was her hair, which was much lighter, 'lifted' with streaks, and also in a freer, more relaxed style. I know for sure that her skin would not have looked as glowing as it did if it was topped by that old, deadening hairstyle and colour.

So what are your options?
Wash-in colour
With pepper-and-salt, or partially grey hair, you can do what I and many of my friends do: use a wash-in colour

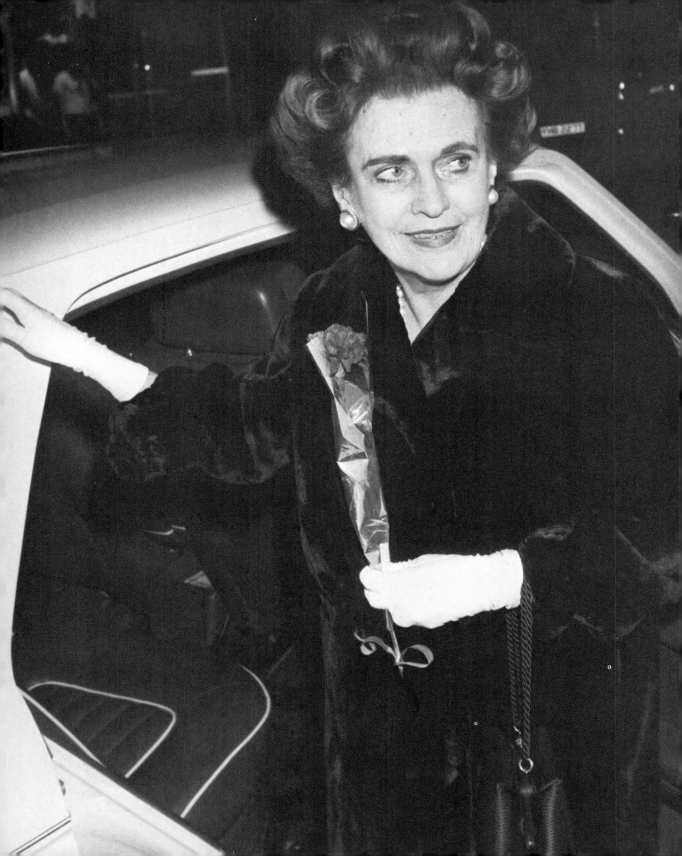

that washes out with the next shampoo. This means you allow your hair to go its own way, but control the final effect. Remember that you are getting marvellous 'free' streaks! Hairdressers have to bleach sections of younger hair if they want to add streaks of colour. Yours has naturally bleached sections. Wash-in colour is perfect for hair that has quite a lot of grey around the temple or in streaks throughout the hair. You can change the grey to honey blonde or light ash and it gives a very pretty frame to the face. Because it washes out I've experimented with a few different colours. I find that shades darker than my own basic hair colour look heavy and make my skin seem sallow. Auburn tints turn orange on my hair. I once tried silver but I didn't like the greyish look it gave to all my hair. I now stick to beige blonde or ash and I'm very pleased with both. One word of warning though – it can take on a brassy tinge in direct sunlight, so keep your head covered.

Keeping the grey
Some women look fantastic with grey hair and it makes them look supremely elegant and distinguished. But the kind of grey hair that is always admired has a beautiful texture, is shining and healthy – and isn't tinged with yellow or blue. It's always beautifully groomed and stylish. If you like this look, you can copy it. Your hairdresser can change the basic grey colour or add different coloured grey streaks to make it more interesting. One woman I know has her steel grey hair highlighted with white and it looks stunning.

Opting for new colours
Sometimes, when hair turns grey it doesn't fit in with the personality. I have a friend who was utterly miserable with grey hair and she literally came to life again once she had it changed to hazel, a few degrees lighter than her original colour. Losing your original colour can also allow you to be

more daring and imaginative with your hair colour. Actress Moira Lister's hair has intriguing shades of pink, mauve and blue which suit her pale skin and, at sixty-one, she doesn't feel it is too way-out.

WIGS

These look so natural nowadays that they are almost indistinguishable from ordinary hair, but the best ones are expensive. If you have to wear one, get the very best you can afford.

The most natural-looking are made-to-order from a combination of human and synthetic hair sewn on to a base. You can buy full wigs or hairpieces.

You should take great care choosing the right colour. If you're having a full wig, choose something a shade or so lighter than your original colour. Always check it in natural daylight, as it can look very different outside the shop.

Don't choose a wig that is much greater in volume than your hair was normally. It will almost certainly look unnatural.

Small matching hairpieces are very useful and easy to wear if you are just needing extra fullness. They are light and comfortable and marvellous to add to a chignon, or to give extra height to a style.

GLASSES

The majority of us wear glasses, if not all the time, at least for reading, knitting or watching TV. Today there is an enormous range of styles and colours to choose from, and the new spectacle shops are designed with plenty of mirror space so that we can see exactly what we look like, and take our time in selecting exactly what we want.

Glasses should be stylish, not purely functional, especially if they're worn all the time. They should look like a well-chosen accessory and can be enormously flattering. With the cost of frames coming down all the time it's worth investing in a wardrobe of glasses with different shapes and colours to suit your colour schemes.

When choosing new frames, stand back and view yourself full length as you would when buying a hat. It's not only your face you have to take into consideration, but your size as well. A big woman doesn't look right in tiny glasses, whereas large owl-shaped ones can overpower a small figure. If you normally wear a hat, take this into consideration. A round hat with round glasses, for example, isn't the best combination.

Not so long ago neutral-coloured frames were considered the best buy because they went with everything. I've always thought them insipid. A dark frame is much kinder to the skin. You can't 'neutralize' glasses, so you might just as well make a feature of them.

There are no hard and fast rules about what suits which face: the only thing is to try them on until you find something you like. Be daring about it! Eveyone should have at least one spare pair of glasses, and this is where you can afford to experiment. Play safe with your usual pair and then go for something completely different. I encouraged a friend of mine to do this – in fact, I pushed her into buying a pair of glasses that she didn't really like as she said they were too large and 'different'. Now she wears those ones all the time, and keeps the others as her spare pair.

Buy something extra-special for evenings. Have frames to complement your favourite outfit – it can look very stylish to tie up a colour combination in this way.

Here are a few practical things to bear in mind:

● Choose a good optician. An opthalmic optician will be checking the health of your eyes as well as your sight.

● Your glasses must fit properly. A good optician will fit them on you and make adjustments so that they are comfortable. Don't leave the shop until you have made sure that they don't press on the nose and cheekbone, and are not tight behind the ears.

● As a guide, the top line of your frame should be level with your eyebrows. Round faces can take frames

---

HAIR HINTS

● To give fair hair a shine, try a camomile rinse. To make your own, pour ½ pint of boiling water over 3 camomile tea bags, boil for ten minutes and allow to cool. Rinse your hair with this after shampooing. This is enough for one generous rinse.

● Lemon juice makes hair shine, whatever its colour. Strain the juice of half a lemon into a cup of luke-warm water, pour over your freshly shampooed hair, and leave on for five minutes. Rinse thoroughly.

● When using rollers, don't pull the hair tight otherwise it can break. You *can* wind the hair tightly round the roller, so long as you make sure the hair between the scalp and the roller is loose.

● Avoid brush rollers on damp hair. They can get tangled up and you'll often find quite a lot of hair comes away with the rollers – use the smooth-sided sort.

● Never colour and perm your hair at the same time, as the different chemical processes involved can cause damage.

● Don't use a medicated shampoo unless it has been prescribed by a doctor for a scalp infection.

● Brushes and combs should have round, smooth ends so they don't scratch the scalp or break the hair.

● If your hair is very dry, don't wash it more than once or twice a week as it can lose too much moisture. If it looks lank, use a dry shampoo in-between times.

● If you use setting lotion after shampooing it can be reactivated the next day by spraying a fine film of water over your hair. This restores some of the bounce.

When choosing glasses, view yourself full length. Your size must be considered as well as the shape of your face.

that are wide and not too deep. Long faces are balanced with large deep frames that are wide at the sides.

● Choose a simple shape. If you want a vibrant colour make sure the frame is thin rather than wide, or it will be too much of a good thing.

● Keep away from rhinestones, winged sides and multi-coloured frames — you don't want to look like Dame Edna Everage!

● If you want to play safe with colours, a narrow black or navy frame is an elegant alternative to tortoiseshell.

● If you wear glasses all the time, invest in a spare pair of tinted lenses, that darken as the light gets brighter, so that your eyes are protected in bright sunlight.

● Don't peer under or over your glasses — that's an ageing mannerism too many people fall into!

TAKING CARE OF YOUR EYES

Regular eye checkups are important.

Have your eyes tested about once every two years – or more often if you think you have problems, or you aren't seeing so well through your glasses.

But eyes can feel tired and sore when there is nothing particularly wrong with them.

Here are some home remedies:

● Blink regularly. It's amazing how we can get into the habit of going for long periods of time without doing such a simple thing. This will sluice the eyes out with tears and freshen them up.

● Rest your eyes by cupping your hands over your closed eyes for a few minutes at a time.

● Splash tired eyes vigorously with cold water while they are open. Lie down with slices of cucumber, or slices of raw potato, or cold, used teabags on your lids for fifteen minutes.

● If you have had something in your eye that has made it sore, make a solution with a teaspoon of salt dissolved in a glass of water and put in a couple of drops every four hours.

● Don't borrow someone else's glasses! It won't do your eyes any harm, but a prescription that is too weak or too strong for you will tire your eyes.

● Keep your glasses in a case when you're not wearing them; never place them face down where they can get scratched. Scratched lenses also tire the eyes. Remember that plastic lenses, though lighter and unbreakable, scratch very easily – even by cleaning with paper tissues, so if you do have plastic lenses, use a proper lens cloth for cleaning.

● Don't prescribe yourself eye drops. Although they can be bought over the counter, you shouldn't diagnose your own eye condition. If your eyes are persistently irritated, consult a doctor.

● Don't get into the habit of using eye drops which claim to add sparkle, either. Too frequent use will do you no good.

TEETH

Few books, even those apparently aimed at older women, make more than a passing mention of teeth. I find this amazing, particularly as we British have a reputation for bad teeth. I won't repeat the usual advice on looking after healthy teeth and keeping them that way, I'm concerned with helping women who have been unlucky with their teeth.

I've never worried about my hair going grey, but from an early age I was determined not to lose my teeth, or if I did to have the very best false ones possible!

Thank goodness that day hasn't come yet. I've taken care of my teeth, avoided sweet things in my diet, and I've been lucky. My dentist tells me that I should be able to keep them to a ripe old age and I'm certainly going to try. In fact, recent statistics show that the number of denture wearers has actually dropped as more and more people are concerned to hang on to their own teeth.

For too long the main concern has been that people who have lost their teeth should be provided with a false pair that fit well and are functional. Dentists have not been interested in aesthetics – but that attitude is now changing. We are increasingly able to have the final say in everything related to the cosmetic side of dentistry.

Some really exciting advances have been made in the last few years – and these are what I want to point out. Those rows of perfectly even, chalk-white teeth which could never look remotely real can be a thing of the past.

The new dentures
Dentures can now be made with a new material which is much stronger,

doesn't discolour, and because it is light-reflective, looks very like the natural colour of teeth. If you like, you can have other things done too. Teeth can be made uneven, crossed over, or even chipped in front for a more natural appearance.

The new bridgework

The normal bridgework is a long and often expensive process of fixing false teeth to existing good ones, using a lot of metal that you can feel in the mouth. Alternatively, people are given removable plates with one or two teeth attached. Now a revolutionary technique has been developed out of space-age technology. A bonding agent was developed for use in spacecraft that sets absolutely everything and it is this glue that is used in the new Maryland Bridge. A metal band is glued on to the back of the false teeth which are then attached by winged ends to the existing good teeth. They are absolutely comfortable to wear, and look totally natural. They don't have to be taken out and feel like your own teeth.

The other bit of good news is that these can be obtained on the National Health. If your dentist isn't aware of these latest methods then you should look for a dentist who is. If, however, you can't find anyone to do it on the National Health you will have to go privately. This *is* expensive, but to my mind it's worth it — I'd personally rather go without a holiday or a new outfit to pay for it!

The British Dental Health Foundation at 88 Gurnards Avenue, Fishermead, Milton Keynes, Bucks, will be able to help you if you have any difficulties. They have a leaflet, *Selecting a Dentist*, which tells you how to shop around until you find the kind of dentist you need. Don't forget to enclose a stamped addressed envelope for a reply about this or any other related problems.

COSMETIC SURGERY

'I suppose,' commented the daughter of

BEAUTY IS . . . QUOTES

'The secret of beauty is in my thinking.' *Linda Evans*, star of DYNASTY

'There's an inner beauty, which is warmth and radiates from within. And there's outer beauty, which is knowing your good points and emphasizing them.' *Trevor Sorbie*, top hairdresser

'I wasn't born beautiful, but I made the most of my thinness, which many girls can do.' *Audrey Hepburn*

'Beauty doesn't automatically make a woman sensual, but sensuality makes a woman, any woman, beautiful.' *Britt Ekland*

'Beauty today doesn't depend on the tilt of a nose, the arch of a brow — it comes from the confidence a woman feels in herself.' *Estee Lauder*

'Beauty is not looking like someone else . . . real beauty is energy and spirit and pride and humour.' *Victoria Principal*

'Obsession with beauty and with the so-called retention of youth is too time consuming and narcissistic to be palatable or practical to me. I pay attention to the upkeep of my health and looks, but not to the detriment of my enjoyment of life.' *Joan Collins*

'I know a girl who looks just at her face in a cabinet mirror. She sees a beautiful face and therefore she thinks she's a beauty. And therefore I think she's a beauty too.' *Andy Warhol*

'My mouth is really too big and my lower lip is far too heavy.' *Brigitte Bardot*

'I have never met a Miss World contestant who didn't hate something about herself.' Former Miss World, *Eva Rueber*

'When I'm feeling good I don't feel that dependent on my looks. But when I'm going through a bad patch I'd hate to lose them.' *Jilly Cooper*

'I suppose I was pretty but I've never seen myself as a beauty. If you keep worrying how you look you get self-centred and lose what really makes a person. An inner glow and vitality are more beautiful than the best face or figure.' *Elizabeth Taylor*

one of my friends when she heard I was writing a book for her mother's age group, 'that it's going to have pages and pages about gruesome face-lifts and all that sort of thing.'

In fact my mind hadn't been working along those lines at all. On the contrary, I have never wanted a face-lift myself, I have always believed in accepting the way one ages and not trying to turn the clock back. But I realize that many women don't agree with me on this, and it is something I should write about.

Who, I wondered, are the people most in favour of altering the face of a normal older person into a mask-like imitation of someone much younger? Most contented older women, even if they could afford it, wouldn't have the operation. Husbands or lovers rarely demand it, but some women feel it necessary for their own benefit, which I feel is sad, especially as the results only last for about five years.

By far the greatest number of women who have cosmetic surgery of any sort are in some way in the public eye, and want to hang on to a younger image.

Having been in the modelling and the television world, I understand all the professional reasons for having eye, chin, nose, ears or what-have-you surgery. Sometimes it's necessary simply to remain in work. But 99% of women don't have that problem, and for that they should be grateful.

However, for some women getting older is traumatic, and I have a number of close friends who feel that way. They want to remain young-looking, and they feel that cosmetic surgery is the only solution. Others may have good reason to want unsightly bags removed from their eyes because they are unattractive and they make them look tired or unwell when they are not.

I know a few women who have had their faces 'done'. In most cases it's successful if it hasn't been too drastic a lift (which is almost always detectable: that's why it's better to have it done earlier rather than later), but after the initial 'Gosh! You do look well!' it's back to square one. If they feel good about themselves then undoubtedly it's a success in their terms – the problem is that it *doesn't* stop the clock, and if that is what they are hoping for, it doesn't take too long for them to feel that somehow it has failed.

If it's something that appeals to you, here are some things to bear in mind:

● Don't be seduced by newspaper and magazine advertisements. If they have to look for clients, it's suspect. Ask your doctor's advice, but if he's not sympathetic, try to get a recommendation from someone who's had cosmetic surgery.

● It's very expensive. Surgery on the eyes can cost around £300 and a complete face-lift anything from £500 – but costs vary from doctor to doctor and country to country.

● Don't forget it *is* an operation, and that risks are involved, right from having the general anaesthetic to suffering long term effects of shock. It can carry with it all the usual post-operation unpleasantness for a number of weeks.

● The final results may not be all you hoped for – and in some cases you could be left with some scarring.

● Don't decide on cosmetic surgery at a time when you are very depressed for other reasons – such as after a divorce. It is not a cure-all for unhappiness. It is most psychologically beneficial when it changes a physical defect. On its own it rarely makes you feel happier.

● If you decide to go ahead, talk it over seriously with the surgeon first. Be wary if he tells you it will be a 100% success – no surgeon can guarantee you anything like that.

Good luck!

MAKE-UP QUESTIONS AND ANSWERS

These are the questions I am most often asked at my shows.

My teeth are dingy and my dentist says that is my natural colour and nothing will change it. I hate drawing attention to them with lipstick, but I know I need to wear it. What colours do you suggest?

Keep away from shades with a yellow tone, or orangey brownish colours. Don't wear an over-bright, glossy lipstick. Choose a soft colour with a matt finish. You can achieve this by dusting over your lipstick with powder.

My eyes tend to puff up from time to time. What is the best way to deal with them?

A good emergency treatment if you're going somewhere special is to lie flat with your feet raised. Make two cold water compresses by soaking pads of tissues in iced water, squeezing them out, and leaving on your eyes for five minutes.

I don't like using mascara as I end up looking a mess. Isn't there an easier way of making my lashes look better?

You could use a touch of Vaseline to make them look glossier and darker – but from experience, I know it doesn't make them grow!

My neck is very dry and crepey. How can I make it smooth?

You can protect it with cream day and night as you do your face. It won't cure

YOUR FACIAL ROUTINE

If you have a regular cleansing and skincare routine, you don't have to give very much more time to your face. But you should:

Pluck your eyebrows every day. The look is for natural brows, so you don't have to reshape yours. The aim is simply to tidy up your own shape by plucking stragglers. Use a good pair of straight-edged tweezers. Hold one edge against the skin, and pull in the direction the hair is growing. This is most easily (and least painfully) done after a bath when the pores are open. If you

nick the skin by mistake, dab with a little antiseptic on cotton wool.

Have a regular facial – perhaps once a month. Giving yourself a facial can be fun and a restful treat, as well as good for your skin.

What you need:

● *If your skin is dry* – a cream mask (buy one or make your own).

● *If your skin is sturdy and not noticeably dry* – a peel-off, or tightening mask.

● cotton wool, soaked in skin tonic or rose water.

● a scarf for your hair.

1. Tie back your hair.
2. Apply your mask according to the instructions. (If using a home made one, cover the face and throat, working upwards to the hairline, but leaving an area of about an inch round your eyes.) Don't put any on your lips either.
3. Spread the mask upwards and outwards with your fingertips, over your face and throat.
4. Relax on your bed for 10-20 minutes with the soaked pads of cotton wool over your eyes.

the problem but it will prevent it from getting worse. Tie a pretty scarf at the neckline of your dresses preferably in a toning colour. This is something Sophia Loren always does, so effectively that I do not know if she has the same problem as you or not!

I am going through the stage of hot flushes and perspire a great deal. Can you advise me on a make-up that stays put all the time?

Put a green-tinted corrective moisturizing base very sparingly on your clean skin. Cover just the areas where you know you are liable to flush. Only use additional moisturizer on the areas you don't cover with the green base, unless your skin is exceptionally dry. Put your normal beige foundation over the top. Brush over with a generous dusting of translucent powder then forget about it! It really is only a minor problem and one that other people rarely notice.

My upper lid droops over the outer edge of my eye. What's the best way to disguise it?

Only put shadow on the lid, not up to the eyebrows. Use a paler shade close to the eye, and fill in above with a darker shade. Smudge the darker shade round the outer corner of the eye in a V shape, and carry the line softly under the lashes.

I want to have my ears pierced. I'm sixty-five, is it risky at my age?

There is an element of risk of infection

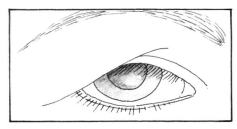

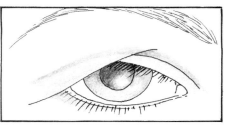

Drooping upper lid, and corrective make-up

5. Remove the mask with plenty of water and cotton wool (or according to the manufacturer's instructions).
6. Pat your skin dry and then apply your moisturizer.

Don't use a mask before a big occasion, or if you have broken or irritated skin.

Masks to make at home
For normal to dry skin
1 egg yolk
1 tablespoon of oil (sunflower or olive)
1 tablespoon of Brewer's Yeast
Mix these ingredients together to form a paste, and then apply.

For very dry skin
1 egg yolk
1 tablespoon honey

1 tablespoon almond oil
Mix together and apply.

at any age. I was unfortunate: I had my ears pierced by a reputable firm when I was sixty, and some hair became wound the sleepers and caused an infection. It is best, if you can, to get your doctor to pierce your ears. If not, at least consult him first. You should not have it done, for instance, if you have a rash, or tiny sebaceous cysts in the earlobes, or if there is a tendency in your family to suffer from scar overgrowth (keloids). Always choose a reputable firm: permanent stands in a main store are often a good choice.

I have very thin lips which I find difficult to make up. Have you any tips?

Apply Lip-Fix first of all. This gives a good base, and gives your lips more definition. It also prevents the lipstick from creeping. Put foundation over your lips, as well as the rest of your face, as this allows the lipstick colour to remain true. Carefully outline your lips with a lip pencil – but don't be tempted to draw a false line to make your mouth look bigger. Fill in with a mid-toned lipstick. Dark colours will make your mouth look smaller, but a touch of darker colour on the centre of the upper and lower lips will make them appear fuller.

What do think about false eyelashes? I'm well into my 60s and I wouldn't be seen without them. When I take them off I feel like a little mouse!

I know other women who feel naked without false eyelashes, but they don't wear the kind that were so popular in the 1960s – those thick, furry strips. The new ones come in feather light strips, or small sections of four or five hairs that you can stick on in small clusters. Both of these kinds look fine and very natural, giving your eyes extra definition without looking too false.

Mascara your own lashes first before applying the false ones, and brush them with an eyelash comb together with your own lashes to blend them. You can extend the strips *very slightly* beyond the eye at the side, to elongate your eye, but if you do it too obviously you will draw attention to the fact that they are false. False lashes only look bad if they are too dark, too thick or too long – in other words, whenever they don't look like your real ones.

I don't like the lines under my eyes. Do you have any disguise tricks for when I want to look my best?

Joan Collins has a good remedy for temporarily smoothing the under-eye area. She suggests brushing egg-white over the lines in a thin film. When it is quite dry, apply your normal make-up. This is rather drying as well as tightening, so you shouldn't do it often, and you should be sure to remove it completely at the end of the evening.

What can I do about my small, deep-set eyes – make-up only seems to draw attention to them?

This is a very common problem. And make-up can help. Using soft, muted colours, you should aim to extend and emphasize the eye with liner and shadow. To do this you should keep your shadow high, away from the lash line. Smudge a soft brown or grey shadow along the crease line, bringing it round the outer corner of the eye. Continue the colour round, lightly smudging it below the lower lashes. Lightly brush a powder blusher from the crease line to your eyebrows. Using an eyeliner, pencil in the palest taupe line as close to your upper and lower lashes as you can. Incidentally, I like to make-up one entire eye at a time, to see the satisfying contrast between the made-up eye and the other!

I have got very deep curves at the side of my nose which I would like to conceal. Is this possible?

You can certainly make them less obvious. After putting on your usual foundation, paint into the dark areas with a very pale (but not white) foundation or concealer stick, using a thin brush. Take your time over it, blending the edges with your normal foundation. Pat off any surplus, and powder in the usual way.

My hair looks so thin, but a perm doesn't seem to be the answer. No matter how gentle it is it always ends up looking frizzy. What do you suggest?

Let me tell you what I did before I decided to grow my very fine hair and wear it up. My hair has never taken a perm successfully either, but like you I need to give it volume. I stopped using a conditioner because it made my hair quite lank, even though I experimented with many different kinds. However, I always used an extra-strong setting lotion (one with a built-in blonde colour for my grey hairs) and I scrunch-dried it – scrunching handfuls of hair until it dried – which gives body. Once dry I put in rollers – whenever I have attempted to set it while it was still damp I haven't got a good shape. This way my hair remained looking full for about six days.

My hair seems to be coming out more now. I wash it every other day as I was told it would stimulate growth, but it doesn't seem to be having any effect. What should I do?

Washing won't stimulate growth, in fact over-washing can dry out the natural oils and cause brittle hair to break off. But there are other reasons for hair loss. Constant slimming is one of them, particularly if your diet is unbalanced – the condition of your hair is affected most by your general health and diet. Too much sun and wind also dry the hair and make it brittle. Remember that hair falls out more in the spring anyway, part of the normal growth cycle. If your hair is fragile then you should treat it very gently – don't apply heat to set it, and try to avoid rollers. Once you are sure that you are doing everything to help your hair, you should see improvement in about two months. But do check with your doctor if you are still worried.

YOUR BODY

When I started modelling it was the era of the New Look, and my figure was considered to be just right: I had the full bust and the tiny waist that showed off the line of the clothes to perfection. My waist was said to be the smallest in London, which also meant that the rest of me was terribly thin. Modelling on the cat walk presented no problems, but out walking with the children I sometimes felt so thin that my spine would jar with every step. I hated my skinny thighs, and I was far from happy in a swimsuit.

A waspie pulled my waist in from its natural twenty-two inch span to nineteen inches, and that was disastrous for my digestion. I used to say that the reason I was so thin was because I always felt sick! It was impossible for me ever to imagine I'd have a weight problem. I'd already had two children, and far from adding the extra pounds and fighting to get rid of them, I was thinner than ever. I didn't exercise. As far as I was concerned there would have been no point. I didn't want to lose weight and that's what we believed exercising was for in those days. As for the health benefits, I don't think anyone ever talked about them.

I started putting on weight in my mid-40s. Since then I have had the same sort of struggle as everyone else to keep it to the level that suits me best. But I am happier with my body in many ways now. I am much healthier than when I was younger, and that's partly to do with the extra weight. I think the very lean look only suits the very young. I have always been an active person, but over the years I have built more exercise into my everyday life with the result that my body is in better tone now than it's ever been.

NO TIME LIKE THE PRESENT

Most young girls want to look perfect, and many are ready to try all manner of diets, exercises and beauty treatments to edge them nearer to their aim. One of the best things about growing up is leaving those days behind, and developing a more realistic view of ourselves, what we look like, and what we *can* look like. The danger is that it's easy to develop a fatalistic attitude after this. There comes a point when some women give up all together. They

Left: This was taken when I had the reputation of owning the smallest waist in London. It was pulled in to about twenty inches with a waspie and practically destroyed my digestion for life.

61

believe there is not much they can do about putting on weight or losing suppleness, or any of the other negative things that can happen. They put it down to *age*.

At my talks there is usually one woman in every gathering who comes over to me at the end and says defiantly, 'Well, I'm quite happy as I am! I suppose you'll say I should lose two stone and take up jogging – but I believe in growing old gracefully!'

They often don't believe me when I say that this is what I believe in too. I would never tell a woman who was genuinely happy with herself and her looks to change a single thing.

But I know that many women are not particularly happy with the way their bodies change as they get older, but they don't know what to do about it, or else they simply believe there is nothing that they *can* do about it. It seems a great shame if they just accept the way they look for these misguided reasons.

In fact your body is even more responsive to care and effort than your face. Women who dedicate themselves to exercise can have incredibly youthful-looking bodies all their lives. I have other things I'd rather do! But the minimum of extra care and efforts can made a substantial difference to any woman, and in this chapter I will outline my ideas on fitness and body care – a basic plan that you can build on if you want to.

WHAT SUITS YOU

Each of us knows when we feel at our best. Ideal weight, in my view, is the weight at which you feel comfortable. I know that when I've been at my biggest, I have not felt good. Before I ever put on weight I assumed that if I did I would just be a larger version of my old self.

But in fact weight accumulates in the least flattering places, such as round the shoulders, the back of the neck, and the top of the arms. The all-over thickening, the feeling of restriction has a slowing down effect on me. I don't move as lightly, I feel stolid and this affects my confidence. For my own well being, I have to make sure that I don't put on too much weight.

Being fit means being able to cope with whatever it is we *have* to do, and everything we *want* to do. You can't feel good in your body if you feel restricted.

I think every woman really knows what weight and which level of fitness suits her best. Think about it carefully and aim for your own particular target. Don't be undermined by what you see and read. The current fitness craze has somewhat distorted people's idea of what a healthy level of fitness is. Some of the most dedicated fitness freaks are seriously endangering their *health* in pursuit of fitness.

It is the same with weight. Quite apart from the pictures of slim young things that can make you feel fat when you are pleasingly plump, there are some myths about weight that contribute to women's doubt as to what is right.

The two main culprits are two common phrases.

One is: 'You can never be too rich or too thin'. This American phrase is often quoted and widely believed – at least in America. I have my doubts that you can never be too rich, but I am quite sure that you *can* be too thin. Extreme thinness is a health hazard. Very thin people, like overweight people, have shorter life spans than those of average weight. Neither do I think that over-thin women look at their best. I can see why couturiers might prefer it – the *clothes* look good, though the same can't always be said for the bodies inside them. A little extra flesh is more womanly, and in my opinion the most flattering and elegant clothes don't need extreme thinness to show them off.

The other often quoted phrase is:

'You gain a pound a year after the age of twenty-five.' Many women believe that this is true and that there is something inevitable in weight gain, that older women were meant to be fat. The truth is that many women do gain weight, but they don't have to. There is no reason, if you have good health, why you shouldn't remain at your best weight throughout your adult life. At the moment there's a surge of anti-thin feeling, and 'big-is-beautiful' is gaining momentum: I'd like to see a compromise between the two.

EATING FOR VITALITY

What constitutes a good healthy diet has changed radically over the years from when I was young. Healthy eating, as it is recognized now, is essentially non-fattening; it makes you feel good and gives you the vitality that keeps you youthful. The foods we are recommended to eat in the sort of proportions that are advised will not in themselves make you fat. The kind of diet that we had during the war is now recognized as being the most healthy way to eat! It doesn't mean we have to go back to austerity foods: a healthy diet can be delicious, and there is an enormous choice. But the rations of butter, meat, eggs, sugar and milk that we were allowed then are now known to be sensible, healthy quantities. Today we have exotic and interesting alternatives, we can make meals that are healthy *and* luxurious.

We need a sensible eating plan for two reasons: for health as well as for the way we look. The two, in fact, are indivisible.

I have changed my own eating habits slowly. After realizing that something is good for me it often takes me a while before I incorporate it into my diet. For instance, I knew that polyunsaturated margarine was healthier than butter, but I remembered the terrible-tasting margarine that we had during the war, and I thought I would never stop eating butter. But I started to buy polyunsaturated margarine for cooking, and occasionally spread the odd bit on my toast. After a while I realized the taste was perfectly pleasant, and now I hardly use butter at all. I introduced brown rice and wholemeal bread into my diet and soon got used to them: they are far more delicious than the white versions. I also eat far less meat than I used to, and find that vegetarian meals can be more interesting than the meat-and-two I previously cooked. I have my son to thank for that. He has a thriving vegetarian restaurant, and the range of exciting dishes he serves has given me plenty of ideas for food to make at home.

THE BASIC HEALTHY EATING PLAN

If you eat moderately according to this plan, with something from each group each day, your diet will be healthy, and you shouldn't put on weight.

Base Your Meal On:
Cereals, bread, flour, pasta, rice, dried peas and beans, pulses, nuts and breakfast cereals. Always choose wholemeal varieties. One of these should be your main ingredient.

A sandwich for lunch, for instance, is a good choice for a meal. The balance of carbohydrate to protein in a cheese and salad sandwich is just right.

Use These As Flavouring Ingredients:
Not more than 4 oz of poultry, rabbit, white and oily fish, liver and kidneys, meat of all kinds, shellfish, eggs.

Eat As Much As You Like Of:
Raw or lightly cooked fruit and vegetables. But watch out for avocados, they are 75% fat.

Include A Little Of:
Low-fat varieties of milk, cheese, cream and yoghurt.

Use Less Than 1 oz Of:
Butter, margarine, cooking fats and oils. Choose polyunsaturated varieties where possible for cooking or salad dressings.

Cut Right Down On
Sugar – and that includes honey, syrup and jam. Salt, and salty foods.

The eating plan I suggest here reflects the current thinking about diet and health. You almost certainly have a well-established eating routine of your own: you are not likely to change it radically if it is very different from what follows. But knowing what you should be eating is a good beginning, and I would suggest doing what I did: changing a little at a time, making one or two meals a week that take into account the healthiest way to eat, and incorporating more as and if you decide you like them. If you are just cooking for yourself it is somewhat easier, but if you have a family you have to take into account their preferences too. On the whole, I have found that most people come to like foods that they know are doing them good.

If you make the changes slowly you are more likely to stick to them. Don't say that you are never going to touch another sweet in your life – if means you will be battling with a decision that never allows you to forget you are on a new eating plan.

Healthy eating also takes into account the way you eat. Look after your digestion. Chew each mouthful slowly and well – chewing is an important part of the digestive process: the saliva also helps to break down the food, and the gastric juices start flowing. Don't jump up immediately after a meal. To aid digestion you need a resting body so that the blood is not diverted from where it is needed most – the digestive organs. Drink plenty of cold (or hot) water between meals but not with meals.

I am not going to break the foods down into their component parts of protein, vitamins, minerals, etc, as I don't think that is the most helpful way of looking at food. There are broadly three categories, in my view. Foods that you can eat as much as you like of, foods that you should eat more of than has been traditional, and foods that you should cut down on.

Eat As Much As You Like Of:

Vegetables and Fruit

These contain essential vitamins and are almost entirely low fat. Not only that, they are some of the best sources of dietary fibre, which is essential for healthy functioning of the bowels and prevents common complaints such as constipation and varicose veins as well as more serious bowel and intestinal diseases. Fibre caught the public imagination a few years ago with the F-Plan diet, which advocated high fibre intake as a slimming aid. It was thought that adding bran to food was essential to obtain the amount of fibre needed, but eating plenty of fruit and

---

THE HEALTHY SLIMMER'S SHOPPING LIST

Eating healthily or losing weight starts in the supermarket. If you buy the right things and avoid the wrong things you will not have to exercise the same will power when you are at your most vulnerable – when you are feeling hungry at home.

● Look for the word *polyunsaturated* when you buy cooking oil, cooking fats and margarine for table use. They contain all the fatty acids you need, but they don't increase the fat or cholesterol levels in the blood.

● Choose the less fatty meats, such as poultry, veal or rabbit, *rather than* pork, beef or lamb.

● Buy more fish: preferably fresh, though frozen will do. When buying canned fish, choose the brands packed with brine rather than oil.

● Buy skimmed, or semi-skimmed milk.

● Buy low fat cheeses: Gouda and Edam are much lower in fat than harder cheeses such as Cheddar. In the range of soft cheeses, Camembert, Brie and cottage cheese are low fat choices. Fromage Blanc and Quark are very good bland susbstitutes for full-fat cream cheeses.

● Use low fat yoghurt instead of cream.

● Change from butter to a low-fat spread. Or buy half-and-half.

vegetables is even better, offering fibre in its most natural form and pleasantly packaged.

I'm sure we all believed that potatoes were fattening. But no, potatoes are full of goodness and natural dietary fibre. A large baked potato is a healthy (and slimming) meal, if served with yoghurt or a low-fat sauce. It is when you cook potatoes with oil (as in chips) or with other fats (as in potatoes mashed with butter and milk) that they become fattening, although they are still nutritious – particularly if the skins are left on.

Sometimes vegetables and fruit are expensive. But pound for pound they are cheaper than meat. Even the most exotic vegetables and fruit cost less than the cheapest cuts of meat. So if you cut down (as you should) on your meat intake, you can spend more on fruit and vegetables. To get the best from them, just bear these points in mind:

● Eat them raw when possible. That way you preserve all the goodness. There are very few vegetables that have to be cooked. Even cabbage, for instance, is nice sliced finely as a winter salad.

● When you cook the vegetables, cook them *lightly*. The vitamins are lost through over-cooking. Use the minimum of water when you boil, and cook until just done, and slightly crunchy.

● Wash, but don't peel, is the rule with almost all fruit and vegetables because a lot of the goodness lies in or under the skin. Chemicals used in growing them are bad for you; therefore all vegetables and fruits should be washed. The only vegetables and fruit that I peel are the ones with skin that is actually inedible.

Eat More Of:

Wholegrains
Bread made with wholemeal flour, wholegrain cereals and brown rice is good for a number of reasons. Grains contain a lot of dietary fibre, and in their unrefined form have more vitamins and minerals – natural goodness – than the white refined varieties.

Peas, Beans and Lentils
All these are protein foods, that contain none of the less healthy animal fat to be found in what we traditionally consider to be protein foods: meats and cheeses. They also contain a lot of fibre. Talk in the past of the 'second class' protein in these foods, made many of us think they were inferior. We now know them as 'incomplete' protein, and putting two together (rice and beans, for example) makes a 'complete' protein, as excellent as anything found in meat.

Fish – Any Kind.
Even the oily fish is a good choice, as fish oils contain nutrients that you don't find elsewhere and they don't contain the unhealthy saturated fats of animal meat.

Poultry
Chicken and turkey are less fatty and therefore better for you than the red meats, such as pork, beef and lamb.

Cut Down On:

Fats
Particularly animal fats (found in meat, cream, eggs, milk and cheese). These are known as 'saturated' fats, and too much in the diet raises your cholesterol level, which contributes to heart disease.

● Trim all fat off meat before cooking.

● Grill instead of frying so that the fat runs off into the pan.

● Or use a non-stick pan and pour the fat away after frying. Frying mince, for instance, you can brown it without fat in your non-stick pan, pour the fat away, and then continue cooking in the normal way.

● If you insist on using some fats in cooking, remember that lard, bacon fat and butter are all saturated fats. Change to oils that are high in polyunsaturated fats, or olive oil which has other active constituents that make it very healthy.

● Cut down on cream – just use it for special occasions.

● Cut down on red meat – even if you cut off all visible fat, there is also hidden fat between the fibres of the meat, and this is high in the elements that make animal fat undesirable.

● Use less butter. Don't add it to fresh-ly boiled vegetables – you'll prefer the taste without it eventually. In cooking switch to using polyunsaturated margarine.

● Spread the thinnest layer of butter on your bread, or change to polyunsaturated margarine, but still use sparingly.

Salt
Too much salt can contribute to high blood pressure. It also makes you retain water, so try cutting down on the quantities you eat.

● Cut down slowly on the quantities of salt you generally use in cooking, accustoming yourself to the difference in flavour before cutting down even further.

● Don't add salt to your plate without tasting your food first.

● Use less bacon and ham – they contain a lot of salt.

● Use fewer tinned foods – most of them have added salt.

● Cut down on crisps and peanuts, which also contain high quantities of salt and fat.

Sugar
Sugar, of course, is bad for your teeth. It has no goodness in it whatsoever, and all it does is add to a weight problem. A sweet tooth usually belongs to a woman who would like to lose weight. If you love sweet things you don't have to think of giving them up altogether, but you should make an effort to cut down.

● Cut down on the amount of sugar you take in tea or coffee – or cut down the *number* of cups you drink.

● Don't have cakes or biscuits every day – only have them once in a while.

● Bake your own cakes or biscuits, choosing recipes that call for less sugar (and fat). Use raw cane sugar instead of white when you do so.

● Check the labels of tinned food; many soups and other savoury items contain added sugar.

● Buy sugar-free jam.

DIETING WITHOUT TEARS

I'm often asked how I keep my figure. In fact I'm a good deal heavier than I used to be, and when I'm careless my weight goes up. My answer is always the same – I have to! I can't talk about sensible eating and keeping fit or looking good if I'm overweight. It used to be the same with models. If they wanted to continue modelling after having a baby they were always right back to size within three months or so. Those who didn't go back to work invariably complained that they'd put on a lot of weight and couldn't lose it.

It was when I was on holiday in Greece one year that I found to my horror the summer clothes I had brought with me didn't fit. That was over fifteen years ago and from that time on I have had to watch my weight. I don't find it easy. My eating habits fluctuate and at times I am ravenously hungry. But I have worked out an eating plan that does work and which bears out my philosophy – that to eat a little less means to weigh a little less so that you never accumulate extra fat which is hard to lose. At the same time I am concerned with the health aspect – eating for vitality and maximum fitness. There is no point in being slim if you look as if you've been ill. Have you ever seen the body of a constant binger and dieter? Let's say it looks better with clothes on. Skin loses its elasticity as it gets older, and if it is continually stretched it won't spring back in the

---

SLIMMING HINTS

There are times when, for no reason you can think of, you feel hungry all the time. It doesn't necessarily follow a pattern. It could be the cold weather or the smell of tempting foods, or a low mood – or none of these. You can wake up feeling hungry and find it difficult to feel satisfied. 'I'm on one of my eating binges', we say in my family, and we have several ways of dealing with it:

● Drink a glass of water when you feel hungry. I always keep a jug of water in the fridge with slices of lemon in it. It's a pleasant drink, it's good for you, and it makes you feel a little less hungry.

● Don't have tempting fatteners in the fridge. Fill it with ready-washed vegetables: carrots, celery, green peppers, mushrooms, cucumber and tomatoes, so that you've always got something ready without resorting to snack foods.

● Don't go shopping while you are feeling hungry. It's easier to resist pastries and sweets on a full stomach. If you do find yourself fancying all manner of things that you should be avoiding, buy *one* small bar of chocolate or similar, and have it as soon as you leave the supermarket. That's better than stocking up on a lot, and having them temptingly in your store cupboard.

● Don't have packets of biscuits, crips, and nuts around in the house.

● Don't skip meals – there is more of a temptation to eat fattening snacks if you do.

● Some of the most fattening foods don't look or taste wicked – and are easy to forget having eaten. Avoid snacks high in calories such as nuts and potato crisps, whatever the flavour.

● Keep a penalty box – for every forbidden thing you eat calculate the cost and put some money in the box. Use it to buy yourself a smaller size item of clothing when you do lose weight.

● The moment your waistband gets tight eat less of everything until it feels comfortable again. Don't give extra weight time to settle.

● Compensate for an overeating binge by eating very little the next day and drinking plenty of water. This is called having your cake but keeping your figure.

same way when you lose weight. But if you reduce slowly you won't have the same problem, and your face won't become thin and haggard.

What you eat is, of course, one of the most important elements in your weight. I don't believe in dieting unless you really have to: in other words, only if you become considerably overweight while eating good healthy food should you have to consider a reducing diet.

You have to work to keep in shape, and if it came without effort there would be no problem. It's so easy to let the weight creep on during the winter months or after a self-indulgent holiday. We nearly all say the same thing when we've put on weight, 'I really don't eat very much. I can't understand it!' It's only when you are keen to shed a few pounds that you realize just how much you *have* been eating.

If you want to lose weight then take your time about it. It's the frantic rush that causes most of the trouble. A slow weight loss is the most natural, it's healthier, and you can measure how much you are losing by the fit of your clothes. The slower the weight loss the more permanent it will be. That is because when you try to lose weight too quickly the body protects itself, as it would if you were being starved:

your metabolism slows right down, and you lose less weight than you had hoped. Once you start eating normally again, the body hoards as much as it can as fat, in case you are in for another period of starvation! Whereas when you aim to lose weight slowly, your metabolism adjusts gently to less food, and the weight stays off when you stop.

It's wanting too much too soon that causes most of the failures. Crash diets make you look awful, feel bad-tempered and are bad for your health. Aim to be smaller rather than bigger at the end of every three months. Stop weighing yourself all the time or counting calories. Get on the scales when your clothes begin to feel a bit loose – certainly not more than once a week. Think of the song 'One Day At a Time', only substitute 'One Pound at a Time'. Get yourself used to a sensible eating plan and stick to it. If you eat less of the fattening foods you are bound to lose weight, so don't be any more impatient than you would be for the seeds you've sown in your garden to start flowering.

The reducing diet that works best is an adaptation of the healthy diet I have already outlined. If you know what is good or bad for you, at least you

COOKING FOR HEALTH

● Substitute honey for sugar – it is twice as sweet so you only need to use half as much.

● Keep washed fruit and vegetables fresh in the fridge in airtight plastic containers.

● When cooking chicken or fish remove the skin first. Skin contains most of the fat.

● Chill all soups and stews that are made with meat. You can then remove all the congealed fat that rises to the top before

thoroughly reheating.

● Don't soak vegetables in water for a long time before cooking, or the vitamins will drain away.

● Use only a little water for boiling vegetables, and save the water for soups and stews.

● Cook cabbage gently. A 'cabbagey smell' comes from too fast or too long cooking – it also means the cabbage has become indigestible.

● If you suffer from flatulence

while you are getting used to a high-fibre diet, or for any other reason, charcoal pills taken with every meal are a great help.

● Keep smoked and processed foods, such as bacon, ham, sausages, kippers to a minimum. They are high in the chemicals nitrate and nitrite, which we are better off without.

● Buy fresh foods in preference to anything tinned or pre-prepared. Most of these have additives, and until we are fully informed as to the effects of them it is better to do without.

hesitate before eating. You should eat according to the healthy guidelines, but *less* of everything, particularly fats and fatty foods. It is far easier to control your eating habits if you don't stick to some strict diet. You should only diet in that way if your doctor prescribes it.

If you eat for health you'll be losing weight in the most enjoyable way, without the nervous tension that makes dieting such a misery. You'll feel fitter, more energetic, more *balanced* in your attitude to food and your weight. You'll want to get out more, and you'll enjoy your food more. This is what will certainly happen to you if you are serious about making the effort.

START TODAY

There really is no time like the present if you need to lose weight. Fix a target at least six months ahead for when you want to be a smaller size. At the beginning of the year, for example, I already have my eye on the summer. I want to look good in a swimsuit as well as in summer clothes. Winter is a good time to start because when you are bundled up in winter clothes it is hard to see what size you are anyway! Watch what you eat to begin with, don't make a big deal of it. If you are used to eating larger quantities than you really need, cutting down drastically might put you off before you start. A little less at the end of each week, even half a pound, adds up as the months go by. It's like those small coins that gather in a purse: they're not worth much singly, but they do grow quite surprisingly if you are not always counting them.

Here are some tips that could help you:

● Keep at it. Be secretive if you like, but each day cut down on something. I know one woman who lost a lot of weight just by cutting out sugar in her tea. Another friend decided to have only skimmed milk, and halve her butter intake. Others friends have switch-ed to low-calorie tonic in their favourite drink, others dilute their wine with soda water in the popular continental fashion. Every little change helps to remove a little fat.

● Eat slowly, chew each mouthful and think about what you are eating. Make a meal of it! Have you ever looked round for that biscuit, convinced you haven't eaten it, because you'd popped it into your mouth without thinking what you were doing?

● Give yourself lots of chewy food, like crunchy vegetables. Food that slips down easily encourages you to eat faster. Lots of chewing makes you feel more satisfied at the end of the meal.

● It helps to eat from a smaller plate, but not so small that you feel deprived. That will help you if you believe that you should always eat everything on your plate, even if you are full.

● Never have second helpings. Eat slowly so that you are the last to finish. It's when you have an empty plate in front of you that you are likely to fill it up again. If you feel you *must* have a second helping, aim to wait ten minutes before you fill your plate. Sometimes you don't realize until you have waited that you have already eaten enough.

● Move your main meal to lunchtime, or eat earlier in the evening. The earlier you eat your heaviest meal, the more possibility you have to 'burn it off'. You are more likely to put on weight if this meal is late in the evening, which is your most inactive time.

● Don't eat standing up, or while you are 'on the go', it is easy to kid yourself that you haven't had much to eat. Sit down, and make it a proper break. Don't work or read or watch television when you eat. Anything that takes your mind off the food makes you less conscious of what you are eating and means that you may miss the moment when you are really full.

● If you are really struggling and can't do it on your own, join a slimming club. *Slimming Magazine*, for one, run clubs all over the country. I write for *Slimming*, and have met many of the group leaders, and the success rate is really cheering. There is no age limit for members, and they can give you the support and encouragement you need if your will power is low, as well as providing you with diet information and regular meetings to keep your spirits up. It is also nice to get together with people who share your problem.

KEEPING IN SHAPE

Exercise

'All this fuss about exercise makes me feel very unfit,' said my friend Virginia. 'Every time I switch on television in the morning or pick up a magazine there's somebody exhorting me to bend and stretch and twist and turn. It makes me tired before I've even started my day. But it's made me feel that I simply *must* start doing something. Have you got any ideas?'

'But,' I said with surprise, 'I would have thought that you, of all people, were someone who exercised. You're so agile I can't believe that you do nothing to keep the way you are.' She happens to be the trimmest, most energetic seventy-year old I know.

We sat down together and went through her daily routine to see if there was some way of incorporating exercises into it. But it became clear that she was as fit as a fiddle because she did, in fact, exercise all day long, although she didn't think of it like that. She walked everywhere, she had a big, old house to look after and few labour-saving devices to help her, and she danced around a lot to the radio!

So although Virginia didn't exercise in the conventional way, she was so active that she kept herself marvellously fit. For instance, she washed her kitchen floor *on her hands and knees* every other day. She found it quicker and more effective than a mop – and she could see better what she was doing. Whatever her reasons (and I certainly don't feel tempted to do the same!) as an exercise for increasing suppleness and using muscles that normally don't get used, it was far better than anything I would be able to recommend. I remember her saying to me years ago that once we reach the age when we have time to sit about that's the time to get up and go – and she takes her own advice.

All the most stimulating people I know are physically active. They don't sit for hours looking at television, confining themselves to four walls I don't think any of them get up with the lark or do half-hour push-ups, but if they have problems which can be alleviated by a particular exercise they go ahead and do it. Ann Melrose, for example, has arthritis in her hands and she exercises them continually with a special squeezer which helps enormously.

One of the reasons that exercise is so popular these days is because it's no longer simply aimed at getting rid of flab, or to make us look like the model on the cover of the beauty books (I'm sure you've noticed how books for older woman, demonstrating how and why exercises are the answer to keeping a young figure, are always full of pictures of young women). Exercising regularly is a question of health, of living longer and of having a more enjoyable life. That is something really worth aiming for.

It should be fun, not hard work. Exercise not only makes you healthier, it also releases hormones that actually change your mood for the better, so it is worth making a determined effort to increase your activity levels. That means simply, getting up off your bottom whenever you can and using your body in the way it was meant to be used. You feel less tired, less tense, more alert – and you'll sleep better at night.

Once you get moving and start feeling really well, you become more ambitious. Being well is the most important ingredient in *enjoying* life. There is no age at which we need to stop making changes in the way we take care of our bodies.

If you do allow yourself to become inactive there are penalties to be paid. If you don't use your muscles, they'll shrink from lack of use, which in turn affects your joints, and results in stiffness. We all know what it's like, I'm sure, to bend over to pick up something from the floor and find we can't quite make it! Stiffness is not a necessary part of ageing. Dis-use is the main culprit. Some regular exercise every day is enough to keep the body agile, which in turn means a life of greater activity. The less active you are the more tired you feel, and in the end it becomes a vicious circle.

Exercise is good for your bones, too – because with exercise you lose less precious calcium which you need to prevent your bones from becoming brittle.

Exercise, of course, means different things to different people. I was amused when Eileen, a young girl who has opened her own dress shop near me, told me her reason for not doing any exercise.

'I'm saving my strength for working in the shop,' she said. 'I don't intend wearing myself out with walking and what have you.' In fact, unlike a machine, the body wears out faster when it's idle than when it's used. She would have had much more energy if she'd spent some of her lunch break walking in the local park.

When I had my grooming school I soon realized that the things least likely to be continued afterwards were exercises and sensible diets. Everyone was very enthusiastic to start with. Unrealistic visions of losing a couple of stone and having a lithe, supple body spurred them on at least for the length of the course. After that it became a one-woman slog. Even my models, who above everything had to have beautiful bodies, did the minimum of exercise.

It's the very word 'exercise' that is often the culprit. When I asked seventy-five-year-old Doreen Lean if she did any particular exercises to keep her trim size-14 figure she replied im-

---

STAYING SLIM

I've asked many women who have kept their good figures for the secret of their slimming success – and they are all very similar. They eat in a way that is healthy most of the time. They don't deny themselves the occasional binge, but always go back to healthy eating afterwards.

These are the main points they have in common:

- they eat lots of vegetables and salads

- they eat more fish than meat

- they eat plenty of fibre: wholemeal bread, bran-rich breakfast cereals, potatoes in their skins, brown rice

- they don't eat fried foods

- they drink plenty of water – but not during meals

- they eat few sugary foods

- they eat little fat – most of them opt for skimmed milk and low fat spreads

- those who like a drink have all considerably reduced their alcohol intake, and use calorie-free mixers

- most of them start the day with breakfast, either an egg, toast, cereal and fruit or fruit juice

- they eat very lightly at lunch time

- they try to make their last meal early in the evening

- they all do some exercise

- they never allow themselves to get more than 5 lbs overweight before doing something about it

mediately 'None at all. And I never have done. Mind you, I'm very active. I walk a great deal (I got rid of my car when I hurt my back) and I do most of my own housework. As you can see, I live in a house with a lot of stairs and I'm up and down them all day long. And I love cooking and gardening and playing with the young grandchildren. I really haven't time for exercises.'

Actress Jean Kent also said that she didn't exercise as such, but she swam and walked a lot!

Ideally that is the way it should be. Exercise should not be done in energetic fits and starts, but should be incorporated into our daily life. It should be associated with the normal routine, and ordinary pleasurable things. Although I know that a good work-out in a gym is sheer heaven for many women (my daughter Vida included), for others it is a nightmare, and it demands an enormous amount of discipline that is difficult for most of use to maintain. Alone, at home, to a tape or just the sound of one's own breathing, it's even harder. Undoubtedly being in

a class with a group of other women and a teacher keeps you going – if you are disciplined enough to get to the class in the first place.

Joan Collins likes traditional exercising. She says, 'For me, exercise is as necessary for survival as eating and drinking. When I don't exercise for a few days I feel sluggish and fat and my body starts to lose its muscle tone.' She works out in a gym, but when she is travelling she does her exercises in the hotel room, dressing room or wherever she finds floor space. She also never uses a lift unless she has to, and walks whenever she can. Jane Fonda has the same kind of dedication, and it certainly shows in the absolute fitness of their bodies.

But we are not super-women, the majority of us. When I read Leslie Kenton's book *Ultra Health* in which she says, 'After twenty-four hours of inactivity your muscle tissues begin to deteriorate' – I feel like crying, 'Too late! too late!' It makes the whole business of exercise an unnecessary burden. That is why I find it cheering

---

VITAMIN SUPPLEMENTS

Some people swear by them, others say that on a good balanced diet you shouldn't need any. I think that this is broadly true, though I have tried many vitamin pills and other supplements throughout my life. There are a few that I still take, and I believe do make a difference.

Garlic Perles
For years this was the only supplement I ever took. Among other things it is a blood purifier and can prevent heart attacks; it helps bronchial conditions; increases resistance to infection; and research in West Germany showed that children who took garlic had safe levels of lead in their blood, even though they lived in cities where other chil-

dren had high lead levels. In perlé form, garlic isn't anti-social and you can take them with a cold drink last thing at night.

Vitamin C
This had an almost immediate effect on me when I started taking 1000mg every day. My skin and hair improved visibly, the whites of my eyes became clear and my body no longer felt stiff. It makes me feel very well all round. It promotes healing and with calcium helps prevent bones from becoming brittle (calcium is to be found chiefly in milk, milk products and vegetables). Another thing that convinced me was that the five top gerontologists working in America (not one under seventy-seven) all take extra supplements

of Vitamin C. They believe, though it is still not proved, that it prevents cancer.

Vitamin E
Research has shown that Vitamin E works with Vitamin C to help strengthen the body's auto-immune system, which means that it is ready to fight illness and is supposed to prolong your healthy life. The dosage should be increased slowly up to 500 IUs a day.

Ask your doctor before prescribing yourself any supplements.

Stiffness at any age can be prevented through a diet low in fat and protein and high in fresh raw foods, combined with regular exercise.

that more and more experts are advocating *activity* exercise, not the mechanical repetition of what seems to me to be tiresome and rather boring movements. Fitness and suppleness can be gained and maintained in many other pleasant ways.

I was recently trying to persuade an old friend of mine to be a bit more consistently active. She is the kind of person who starts something with great enthusiasm and then quickly becomes bored and does nothing at all.

'I wouldn't mind trying these aerobics,' she said, 'They sound quite different.' She had no idea what aerobics were but she thought they must be a revolutionary new system. When I told her that aerobic exercise is anything you do that gets your heart pumping fast and your lungs working so that you feel slightly breathless she was clearly disappointed.

'But it means you can do anything that appeals to you,' I said, 'like dancing, or swimming or playing tennis.'

'I don't like any of those things, you know that' she replied.

'Or if you're really keen you can work away to an exercise tape, or run up and downstairs – it doesn't make any difference,' I went on, 'the end result is the same – increased stamina and fitness.'

I didn't have any success persuading her, because she really prefers to think that exercise is something difficult and apart from normal daily life – then she doesn't have to feel bad when she gives up.

I asked Lotte Berk, affectionately known as 'The Queen of Exercise', if she was still exercising every day. Lotte used to demonstrate her unique methods to my model students before she opened her famous studios in London and New York. At seventy-three she still has the same slim, lithe body she had then.

'Not so much as I used to do, but I concentrate on my stomach exercises, which have the effect of strengthening my back – the area where many women of my age have problems. I go to the studio every day. My students are my life – I love to be with people.' Lotte's students have included, amongst many other famous personalities, Barbara Streisand, Britt Ekland, Joan Collins and Carol Linley.

As with dieting, there has been an over-abundance of conflicting advice about what exercises we should do, and for how long we should do them if they are going to be of any benefit to us. But most experts are agreed on one thing – that it is far better to exercise regularly than have bursts of activity just at the weekends, for example. Doing a few basic exercises every day is far better than half an hour's violent exercise. Because I am only too aware that most of us do not stick to the regular daily dozen, I am giving my own ideas and beliefs about keeping fit during the course of each day. As with any activity that is new to you, you should ask your doctor first if you are in any doubt.

The good thing to remember is that you don't need to do anything complicated to raise your level of fitness. My suggestions, I believe, are easy to carry out unless you are in poor health, and you should feel the benefit of them really quickly.

Walking
Walking is my number one favourite exercise, and I am not alone in this. A brisk daily walk (you can start by not being so brisk if you're out of practise!) is an excellent way to send the blood pumping round the body, keeping the heart muscles in working order. It is the single exercise *all* doctors recommend, not just because it is so gentle or easy to do, but because it really is one of the best and most effective exercises. The famous *Pritikin Programme for Diet and Exercise* is one among many books that say, 'The main exercise we recommend (in fact you don't have to do anything else) is regular sustained

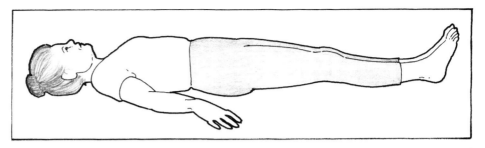

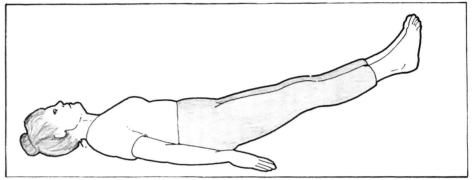

Exercise to strengthen stomach muscles

Right: Jean Kent. Actress, born 1921. She wears her hair attractively short nowadays, and just the simplest of earrings, but the whole effect is softened by the soft spotted bow at the neckline.

'I like to keep fit' she says. 'I don't diet, but I do keep a watchful eye on what I eat, and although I don't do formal exercises I walk and swim, do plenty of gardening and house work. I've been very lucky. I did the things I wanted to do and now I'm spacing out my time to fit in with my other interests. Every age has its own pleasures.'

walking.'

Walking has just about everything to recommend it. It stretches the spine and doesn't distort the body, and you burn up as many calories walking a mile as running a mile. Indeed, it has all the benefits of jogging without any of the drawbacks – jogging must be done

BRITISH MEDICAL ASSOCIATION REPORT 1986

In a report aimed at reducing diet-related diseases, particularly heart diseases, the BMA called for:

● a 50% reduction in the average sugar intake

● a 25% reduction in the average salt intake

● a 50% increase in dietary fibre

● alcohol intake reduced to twelve units per week (the equivalent of twelve glasses of wine, or six doubles)

correctly, or you will jar your knees, strain a tendon, etc. No one need fear damaging themselves when it comes to walking. The more you walk, the more it helps you to move gracefully.

For years I opted out of every keep fit class that ever took place in my school on the excuse that I was too busy. I was too thin, I told myself, I didn't need to lose any more weight, and I was always too tired. Today I am fitter than I've ever been. I don't do anything drastic, but I am intensely aware of keeping my body supple. I walk wherever I can: in proper shoes so that I can stride out without restriction. At first I only strolled for about ten minutes at a time, building up to a faster speed and a longer time, until today I can walk without feeling tired for an almost indefinite period. When I have a headache, or feel tense or even unusually tired, I walk.

My mother is eighty-seven and much fitter and more active than many women twenty years or more her junior. She goes out for a walk every day – even if the weather is atrocious. On those occasions she possibly only

manages half an hour instead of the hour or more that she usually does. She often has visitors to stay and they accompany her on her walks. 'I feel so much better!' they tell her. 'The fresh air and exercise have done me the world of good!' Most of them believe that they have done enough healthy exercise to last them until the next visit.

The remarkable eighty-five-year-old, Barbarba Cartland, not only walks as often as she can in the open air of the country side but believes that enjoying the beauty of her surroundings is an integral part of feeling well. I couldn't agree more. Even if you live in the heart of the city, as I do, there is as much to see and enjoy in the streets as in the city parks and gardens. You can get up and go in every kind of weather – and unlike some forms of exercise, you don't need any special equipment. It's part of Sophia Loren's exercise routine, 'I stretch, walk and take care of my trouble spots,' she says. Whatever else they may do, almost every fit, active woman I ask says she walks a lot.

● If you drive, aim to leave the car behind for all but the most essential journeys.

● Give yourself a walking errand at least once a day – say to the post office, or to the baker for a loaf of bread. It is easier if you haven't developed a love for walking to have an end in mind, rather than striding out just for the pleasure or the exercise.

● Take public transport rather than your car – but don't wait at your nearest stop – walk to the next one, or get off a stop before your final destination.

● If you are stuck inside most of the day, whether at home or at work, then move about as much as you can. At work, don't use the internal phone, walk to see colleagues. Use the stairs rather than the lift. At home, don't get into the habit of asking other people to run errands for you. If you want something – go and get it. And if you have to keep going upstairs to fetch things you have forgotten, think of the good it is doing you!

● Get more pleasure from your walks by really noticing what is happening around you. For instance, I like watching the changes in my area. If a house is being done up I'm curious to see how it is getting on, and I take new turnings rather than the same old routes, to investigate the shops.

● When you do take the car, use it to take you to a beauty spot, then leave it and walk. Go with a friend and take a light picnic.

● If you really get the walking bug, join a club and meet other people who feel the same way as you do about it. Orienteering is a sport that appeals to walkers. You have to find your way over a given stretch of land by following a map and using a compass. Many orienteers do it as a run to get the fastest time, but there is no reason why you can't enjoy the activity, even if you finish last.

● Remember that a game of golf involves, on average, a five-mile walk.

● Choose good, proper walking shoes. Ann Melrose recommends Clark's Walkers. She says, 'I can literally walk for miles when wearing these shoes without feeling tired. They have sorbothane soles and absorb three or four graveties. You can't jar yourself even if you are walking on the hardest pavements.'

An alternative is a pair of the good running shoes made for joggers. There are many excellent brands, and it is worth getting them from a sports shop.

Swimming
I used to swim a lot when I was younger, and it always gave me a great sense

of well being. My mother insists that the reason I am 'so strong' is because as a child I lived abroad and swimming was part of my daily life. But then, inevitably, I slackened off. The only time I found myself near water was on holiday, when I would spend my time inert, sunbathing, with just the odd five-minute swim from time to time. But when a spanking new swimming pool opened five minutes from where I live a couple of years ago, I took it up again.

It is a marvellous exercise for you at any age, even if you are in a fragile state of health. It uses every single muscle in the body, but gently. This is because the water cushions you from the effects of gravity, and doesn't allow sudden, jerky movements.

The general health benefits are unquestionable, with increased mobility in your joints, and a general improvement in suppleness. Pushing yourself that little bit more, so that you are slightly out-of-breath after ten minutes energetic swimming, shows that it can be a marvellous 'aerobic' exercise too. But some people find even more startling improvements in particular conditions.

One woman I met in my local swimming pool told me she was virtually crippled with arthritis – she was hardly able to walk and was on very heavy medication – until she took up swimming every morning. Now she takes no drugs at all, she can walk again and hardly suffers any pain. She is so excited by this change in her life that she believes life really does begin at sixty. Every morning she turns up for her swim fully made-up, hair immaculate and wearing false eyelashes!

You don't have to be a good swimmer to feel the benefits of a regular dip in the pool. You don't even have to be able to swim at all.

The arthritis sufferer could swim, but it was months before she felt able to leave the side of the pool. To begin with she simply worked on doing underwater exercises, hanging on to the rail and kicking her legs, until she felt some of the mobility return. Now she swims confidently up and down, three or four lengths without stopping.

If you can't swim, it really is never too late to learn enough to get you from one end of the pool to the other without putting your feet down. Either join a beginners' class at your local pool, or ask a friend to teach you. I taught my friend Ann Ladbury, the dressmaking wizard, to swim when we were on holiday in Italy a couple of years ago. I had no idea that she couldn't swim – she had a wardrobe

---

TASTE ENHANCERS

If you are cutting down on sugar and salt you will want to add flavour in other ways.

● Use more herbs and spices. You will not notice the lack of salt if you have extra flavour in this way.

● Lemon juice gives a tang to savoury dishes.

● Soy sauce enhances flavour as salt does – try to buy the sodium-free variety.

● If you have a craving for chocolate try substituting it with carob.

● Carrots are a natural sweetener. If sugar is called for in a savoury dish (such as tomato sauce) try adding chopped or grated carrot.

● If you like to start the day with something sweet on your toast, make your own compote by blending Californian raisins in your mixer with a little water to make a spreading consistency. It is delicious, only contains natural fruit sugar, and is full of vitamins.

● Use molasses instead of golden syrup. It is much stronger tasting which means you can use smaller quantities. It is full of valuable minerals and has fewer calories than other sweeteners. You can also use it in the place of sugar for making cakes.

● In sweet dishes compensate for less sugar by using spices such as nutmeg, mace and cinnamon.

full of swimsuits of every style and colour, none of which had ever been near the water!

'I'm terrified,' she said, when I tried to coax her into the water. 'I've wanted to swim all my life, but I wouldn't dare try.' She had even been too embarrassed to let anyone know her 'secret' as she'd felt silly. In fact, I could only get her into the water by telling her that

nobody was in the least bit interested in watching her. By the time we were ready to have our mid-morning snack she could swim! Only a few strokes to begin with, but she improved rapidly each day. It has been a real bonus for her. Now when she goes on her tours round the country she looks for a hotel with a swimming pool and gets in a bit of exercise at the same time.

● Swimming is aerobic exercise, a muscle strengthener and an improver of flexibility.

● Aim to go to the pool at least once a week: if you enjoy it, increase it to three times.

● Choose a time when the pool is least busy: early in the morning is often a good time, though it's when the dedicated swimmers go so you may feel uncomfortable if you are a poor swimmer. Ask about adult-only evenings, or slack times during the day if your day is flexible.

RELAXATION

Relaxation is as important as exercise – and can be as much of an effort. Sitting tensely, with your arms crossed, even if you are doing nothing, is *not* relaxing.

'Why don't you just relax?' People say when we are in the middle of some work or domestic crisis, or when our energy is at its lowest ebb.

'I am relaxed!' we usually snap back, while our shoulders are aching with tension, and our minds whirling.

Tension is the great enemy of beauty, the robber of sound sleep, the underminer of health and vitality. Learning to recognize the symptoms means that you can do something about it before it becomes too overwhelming.

Each of us develops our own way of coping with stress, but the methods we choose can often be self-defeating. The gin-and-tonic in the evening won't effect a cure, though if you believe it does then the temptation is to go on and on. Similarly, until recently doctors were handing out tranquilizers to women with any problems as if they were the great cure-all. But they cause dependency and, as with other drugs, many women feel so bad when they try to stop taking them that they continue taking them just so they don't feel terrible – not to feel better.

Real relaxation involves soft, limp muscles and an almost blank mind. Learning to reach this state at will is one of the finest ways of combating

Left: Ann Ladbury. She has cut her long thick blonde hair and now wears it sweeping up and off her face, a much more rejuvenating line particularly since she has put on some extra weight. 'It runs in the family,' she says, 'and I have to be very careful what I eat. I always fast one day a week and this helps to keep my weight down.'

Known as television's dressmaker, Ann almost succeeded in teaching me to sew when we were together on the STV series Houseparty and in return I taught her to swim shortly after her fiftieth birthday!

THE BENEFITS OF BEING PHYSICALLY ACTIVE

Stronger Lungs
Physical exercise that results in you being out of breath gradually increases the size and elasticity of your lungs, which means you can breathe more deeply and slowly, which in turn gives you vitality.

Stronger Heart
Like any other muscle, the heart muscle becomes stronger the more it has to work. That means it can pump more blood round the body with each beat, so that it can beat more slowly. The arteries open up, and blood pressure lowers.

Better Digestion
As the body is tuned up, the whole digestive system gets to work more efficiently, combating constipation and helping us get the maximum benefit from our food.

Suppresses the Appetite
Good news if you're keeping an eye on your weight. You won't feel in need of food for a good two or three hours after brisk exercise.

Better Complexion
The skin benefits from the improvement in your circulation, keeping it supple. It also gives a healthy glow no cosmetic can supply.

Stronger Muscles
This means a better shape and less fat.

A Calmer Outlook
You feel much happier after any kind of exercise. It gets rid of pent-up energy and you can really enjoy the relaxation afterwards. It helps to promote restful sleep.

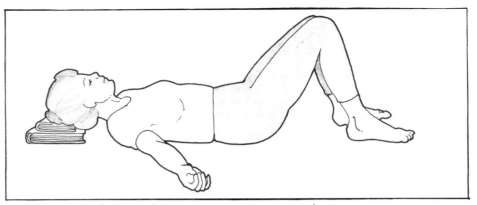

The Alexander Technique – lying down in the correct position

excess stress and conserving our energies for when we need them most. When the body is in a totally relaxed state it is virtually impossible for the mind to feel panic and feelings of anxiety start to subside; your heart-rate returns to normal; everything looks brighter. You don't have to aim for this state of complete relaxation every time. Sometimes it is enough to do something soothing, to stop the build-up of tension.

Walking

Walking doubles as both exercise and a relaxant – particularly if you are tense because you have something on your mind. Sometimes it helps just to stride out and let your mind tick over any problems that needs solving. At other times you want to have your mind taken off your problems so it is worth taking a detour to find someone to chat to. I like to walk to the market in certain moods, because the back-chat of the cheeky stallholders is a real tonic.

Doing Nothing

This is an art, believe it or not, because most of us feel guilty if we set out simply to pamper ourselves. When you are very busy it seems particularly time wasting to do this, but in fact it is very constructive. If you become overly wound up you will not function effectively, whereas a couple of hours switched off can make all the difference to your performance.

One of the best ways to do this is to take a long bath (see the Body Care section). Use the time when you are having a long warm soak to read or simply lie back with your eyes shut if you prefer. Following on from this it is worth taking the opportunity to do something pleasantly enjoyable but relatively mindless, like giving yourself a manicure or other 'body maintenance' that appeals to you. This kind of activity usually leaves you feeling good about yourself, which is another sure way to combat tension.

Other similar ways to do nothing effectively include putting your feet up and listening to some soothing music, or even going to bed in a nice warm bedroom with a pile of magazines. Everyone needs to find out which *in*-activity makes them feel completely relaxed, and make a of point of indulging in it at the appropriate time.

Keeping Busy

This sounds like quite the opposite advice but it is sometimes the way to help you unwind if you choose the right activity. I find that something that demands concentration, such as knitting, painting or embroidery really does help combat tension. It is amazing how the constant rhythm of knitting, for example, relaxes the body and the mind so that you have little opportunity to tense yourself or think depressing thoughts. Seeing the results of your labours also has an uplifting effect, which is why a friend of mine chooses to do her gardening as a relaxing hobby.

The Total Blank

This is what you should aim for when things really get too much for you — complete rest for mind and body. Even twenty minutes — if you really let yourself go — will make you feel very much better.

First write down a list of everything that is on your mind (including things that you have no power to control, such as nuclear war!), making a list of all that you have to do or worry about. Once every single thing is written down, you will find that your mind stops buzzing with them, at least for the length of your rest.

Then you should lie down, on the floor, in a position that I learnt when I was being taught the Alexander Technique (a postural retraining that helps, among other things to combat tension).

Get a thick book (like a large dictionary) or two thinner books for your head. Lie back, with your head propped by the book, and tuck your chin in slightly. This tilts your head to the correct angle, which is also the most restful angle — more restful, in fact,

than a pile of pillows. Now bend your knees, so that your feet are flat against the floor, and your knees pointing up to the ceiling. This tucks in your pelvis, so that your spine is flat against the floor. Test this by trying to slide your hand between the small of your back and the floor. If you *can* get your hand between, shuffle your bottom a little further down, until the gap closes. When your spine is flat like this all the muscles in your back are in the correct position, and don't have to strain — which eases pain and tension in the back. Let your arms lie loosely at your sides, with your hands facing towards the floor, your fingers open and loosely curled.

At this point, I depart from the Alexander Technique. I believe that unless you have an Alexander teacher manipulating you in this position, some of your muscles are bound to be tense.

With your eyes shut, make a mental inventory of your body, starting from your feet. Think about whether the muscles are tense. Check by consciously tensing the muscles and then letting them go: that is how they should be feeling all of the time. Thinking like this, work your way up your body. Are your shoulders holding themselves rigidly off the floor? Think about them having weights on them, and slowly

sinking downwards towards the floor. Feel the tension ease in your neck muscles as your shoulders relax.

Is your jaw clamped shut? Let your mouth fall open slightly, and feel your tongue suspended in the middle, the tip just touching your front teeth.

When you have assured yourself that every part of your body is as relaxed as it can be, lie still in this position for about 15-20 minutes. You don't have to fall asleep to feel the benefit of it. Try to keep your mind totally blank — have a tape of soothing music on if this helps.

When you are ready to get up, don't do this suddenly. Raise youself to a sitting position first of all, and when you are accustomed to this, slowly bring yourself to standing.

Doing this every day, tense or not, is very good for you. Some people like to re-orientate themselves like this, after a busy day and before preparing to go out.

BODY CARE

Bodies respond well to pampering. Body skin, because it is usually hardly ever exposed to the daylight and is fairly tough, ages much slower than the skin on the face. Body care is an entirely pleasant experience — it doesn't involve all that close peering into mirrors, and is usually quiet and relaxing.

Bathing

Most of your beauty care can take place at bath time. Whether you bath or shower is a matter of choice — they are both good for different reasons.

A shower is undoubtedly the best way to get yourself clean quickly and efficiently. It is also invigorating, improves the tone of your skin and stimulates the circultion. A shower gets you going in the morning like nothing else.

A bath, on the other hand, is not such an efficient cleansing aid, unless you rinse down afterwards (fragments

EXERCISING WITHOUT EXERCISE

Your muscles and joints can be exercised without an exercise programme. These are some of the ways:

Climbing stairs

With every step you climb you are lifting your entire body weight, and stair climbing gets your heart and lungs working to capacity. Don't lose any opportunity to climb stairs — you can take them at the pace that suits you best, or hang on to a rail if it helps. If you feel agile enough, take two stairs at a time.

Spring-cleaning

Or cleaning at any time of year, uses muscles that are otherwise under-used. Stretching up to take jars down from shelves, cleaning inside low-set cupboards are activities that help

your general level of fitness.

Gardening

The whole range of jobs you have to do to maintain your garden are excellent for keeping you fit: digging, weeding, pruning, and taking the wheelbarrow from one end of the garden to the other. It helps that all this happens in the open air too.

Decorating

Either doing it yourself, or helping someone more skilled is marvellous exercise. I always thought I was built in such a way that it was impossible for me to touch my toes, so I gave myself quite a shock one day while demonstrating this impossibility to someone. I found myself touching them easily, without the slightest strain in my back. I had been doing a lot of decorating at the time, specifically preparing and painting a ceiling,

and the stretching involved had had that unlooked-for side-effect.

There are movements that you can do throughout the day, when it occurs to you, that will improve your muscle tone or general heath, without you setting aside time specifically to exercise.

- Pull in your stomach muscles at any time of the day. This strengthens the muscles, stimulates the blood circulation, helps prevent constipation and helps stop fat being deposited round your middle.

- Keep a little rubber ball handy — one about two inches in diameter, and from time to time squeeze it to the count of four, then release. Do this four of five times with each hand. It will strengthen your hands, wrists

of soap, soapless cleanser or oil otherwise remain on your skin). But it is marvellously relaxing, especially if you use bath salts, and is the best way of winding down in the evening before bed. You can also introduce skin treatments, such as special oil, into the water.

Whether you prefer a shower or a bath, don't use water that is too hot. Very hot water is drying for the skin; it causes spider veins to appear on the skin, and is not good for varicose veins; too hot water also causes breasts to sag.

Don't stay in the water for longer than twenty minutes, and unless you are very tired make good use of your time in the bath. With a good mild soap or soap substitute, scrub your back with a long-handled bath brush or a bath 'strap' made of abrasive material, which you use with both hands in a see-saw movement, to massage body skin. Give your arms and

legs the same treatment with a loofah, or rough hand mitt. This makes the body tingle, improves the circulation, and exfoliates the skin, making it smoother and receptive to the creams you rub in afterwards. Use a pumice stone on rough parts of the feet, the elbows and the knees.

When you get out of the bath, give yourself a brisk rub down with a firm towel, and moisturize well afterwards.

Because bathing is drying for the skin, it is best not to do it every day. A good wash down is sufficient in between times.

The best time to feed the skin is during and after a warm bath or shower, when the pores are open and able to absorb everything more easily. Cheap cream is just as effective as a more expensive product.

Deodorants

Everybody sweats. It is perfectly healthy and natural, and unless the per-

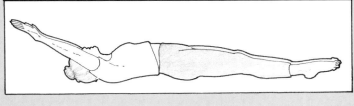

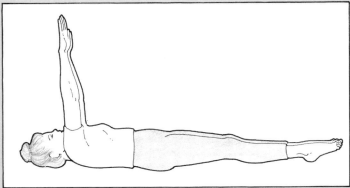

they will go aiming to touch the wall opposite. Then relax. Do this a number of times, relaxing in between. Then stretch your arms out to the side as far as they will go, relaxing as before. Clasp your hands together and raise your arms up and down. Do these loosening up exercises quite slowly, perhaps while you are listening to the radio. During the day, stretch from time to time, you will find it very invigorating.

● If you want to be particularly supple for any reason you can usually achieve it. Claire Kitchen always prided herself on her suppleness, proved by the fact that she could wash her feet in the handbasin! That had to stop when she broke her hip. But it was her ambition to regain the ability to do this — and she managed it after years of walking with a stick, when she was over sixty.

and fingers. I do this in bed before I get up in the morning, then I shake my hands vigorously. It's very good for relieving stiffness.

● Stretch. Before you get out of bed, stretch your legs as far as

spiration is trapped next to the skin where the air can't get to it, it is practically odourless. Most body odour comes from under the arms and the feet, because these are closed-in areas and deodorants need to be used to make sure it isn't unpleasant.

You should, of course, wash under your arms every day, whether you have a bath or not, and wear clean clothes next to the skin. Apply a deodorant after washing, but wait for twenty minutes if you've just come out of a bath. The body needs to be cool if it is to be most effective. Apply the deodorant in the morning and again in the evening if necessary.

If you sweat excessively then you need to use an anti-perspirant. You can buy these 'fragrance-free' or with a deodorant combined.

Sweating is as often stimulated by nerves as excessive heat. If this is so in your case you can give yourself extra protection by wearing dress shields in your clothes. Knowing you are protected in this way often stops the perspiration altogether.

A fashion writer gave me a good tip many years ago. She said that if an anti-perspirant is used last thing at night and then applied again in the morning it would be just about 100%

effective. I certainly found it worked when I had something particularly nerve-wracking to do.

Don't use a deodorant for at least twelve hours after shaving under the arms as it can irritate the skin.

Deodorant foot powders are very effective only if they are combined with scrupulous cleanliness and frequent changes of tights. If you have a serious problem, bathe your feet in hot water to which foot-bath salts have been added, and after thoroughly drying, dust them with powder. In hot weather dab your feet with surgical spirit before powdering. You can also buy shoe liners, such as 'Odor Eaters', which stop the unpleasant smell.

Vaginal deodorants were in vogue about ten years ago. They are now seen to be more dangerous than effective. Ordinary washing is all you need in this area.

Hands

Our hands age quicker than any other part of the body, and it's not surprising. Even if we have led a life of ease our hands are still constantly exposed and in use. They are not usually protected in the way our faces are, or kept covered up most of the time, as our bodies are. Hands are in and out of

---

HAND PROBLEMS

Swollen Veins
A common problem is veins swelling and standing out on the hands when you are hot. To avoid this, you should make sure that you are not wearing anything constricting around your wrists. Sometimes a watch strap or bracelet is too tight in the hot weather. Don't let your hands drag down at your side for too long, letting the blood run into them.

Before doing photographs in hot weather, models hold their hands up above their heads —

obviously this is impractical, but you can keep your hands propped up on your elbows if you are sitting down, so that the blood flows away from them. Whenever you have the opportunity, run your wrists and hands under cold water.

Brown Spots
Some people are more prone to these than others. Although some people call them age spots, they can, in fact, happen at any age – particularly if you are pale and freckly – and they can be the fault of the Pill. I have them, but they are getting lighter these

days, not because I do anything to bleach them but because I always protect my hands with sun block cream.

Massaging lemon juice into the spots bleaches them a little. I also know women who swear by Vitamin E oil, breaking open a capsule and rubbing it into the backs of their hands.

Merle Oberon used to squeeze lemon juice onto mother of pearl and leave it overnight. The juice corroded the stone slightly, and she would then rub it over the backs of her hands. She swore that this bleached the spots substantially.

water, we garden with them, use them to cook, to sew and to do tough and dirty jobs around the house. Hands show character and personality traits, much as the face does. They don't have to be perfect or young-looking to be interesting, but beautiful hands are always admired and are a source of envy.

I hardly ever noticed if a hand was beautifully cared for until I became a model agent and represented girls who were hand models. I had been too interested in palmistry before that to notice anything more than the shape of the hand and the fingers, and of course the lines on the hand.

I wish now that I had taken more care of mine, that I had worn gloves in the cold weather and covered them with sun cream when it was hot. I rarely could be bothered to wear rubber gloves for washing up, or cotton ones when gardening. The skin on the back of the hands is very thin and stretches easily – and it doesn't spring back into shape. But, as with everything else, it's never too late to start taking care, and it's remarkable how quickly they respond to treatment.

The most neglected nails and hands improve almost overnight if you massage manicure cream in whenever you wash your hands. I carry a handbag size container with me everywhere and use it whenever my hands feel in need. It's especially good in cold weather when the cuticles crack and the skin feels very rough. I find I don't need any other treatment. I now wear rubber gloves to cut down the damage caused by detergents and cotton gardening gloves for any outdoor work. Massaging the cream into the nails improves both the colour and texture as well, but I give them a coat of colourless varnish for extra protection.

I've had brittle nails for as long as I can remember and two years of eating chunks of jelly (which was supposed to strengthen them) didn't make the slightest difference. Nothing has helped, and although I care for them

more regularly than ever before, they still break off. I have now settled for nails that come just to the top of my fingers, and I keep them well-manicured. Short nails have to be particularly well looked after or they tend to look neglected, I rarely use colour on my nails. Coloured nail varnish calls for beautiful hands and nails, otherwise I think it is better to leave them natural. If you have got beautiful hands and nails do show them off to their best advantage with pretty varnish and attractive rings.

● Have rubber gloves one size larger than you need and wear cotton gloves inside to absorb perspiration. Or buy them ready lined.

● Keep your hands out of water as much as possible. When you wash them use a mild soap or soapless cleansing block. Dry them thoroughly on a clean towel, and reapply hand cream every time.

● If your hands are excessively dry, try the bran treatment. You can get bran from the chemist or health shops. Wet your hands, dip them in the bran and rub thoroughly to soften and cleanse the skin. Rinse off, dry well and then rub in hand cream.

● Wear gloves when you go out, particularly when carrying shopping or when it's cold or wet.

Taking Care of Your Feet
No amount of relaxation techniques will help if your feet are killing you. Nothing shows more on the face than the agony of corns, blisters or tight shoes.

I have friends whose feet cause them more misery than anything else, and one woman I know has had to give up her stage career because she finds it too painful to be on her feet for any length of time. It is impossible for us to imagine how agonizing it can be unless

Right: Dynamic 63-year-old Cyd Charisse is still high kicking in the London musical Charlie Girl. *Simplicity, again, is what distinguishes her from the crowd. The relaxed, youthful hairstyle, cut to just above chin length, has that casual air which is dateless. The long line of her jacket gives length to her neck while the pretty necklace follows the line of her blouse, making a frame for her face. 'My work keeps me fit,' she says, 'but when I'm not in a show I still keep up with some of my exercises.'*

we've had a bad corn or sprained an ankle or tried to walk any distance in tight shoes that are rubbing the backs of our heels and pinching our toes!

Most of the problems are caused by badly fitting shoes, but when we are young we usually don't heed the warnings if it means going without a pair of shoes that are fashionable. I don't know how I have managed to keep healthy feet. It must be a combination of luck, and the fact that I have always walked barefoot whenever possible. During my modelling days I often had to squeeze into shoes far too small for me when I was doing shows. For years I bought size 5½ shoes, and *expected* them to pinch and be uncomfortable. Today I wear shoes at least a size larger, and it would never occur to me to worry about my feet looking big in them. At one time that was the most important consideration. It was considered most unattractive to have big feet.

Even if you have given up choosing shoes only for fashion reasons, the damage may have been done years ago – not only by badly-fitting shoes or too-high heels, but by not walking sufficiently. Foot muscles, like all other muscles, literally weaken from lack of use. But with the proper shoes, and the right care you can improve your feet.

Choosing the Right Shoes

Tight shoes deform the feet, and shoes with heels that are too high cramp the toes, cause mis-use of the muscles in the feet and throw your spine out.

Shoes and sandals that are too lose at the sides and back allow the feet to jerk forward when you walk, causing pressure on joints and skin. Most of the callouses and enlarged toe joints are caused by too loose shoes, as are those thickened toe nails which are very hard to cut and look after.

Shoes need to fit snugly and be wide enough across the toes to stop any pinching. It's always better to have the uppers made of leather as it is more flexible and doesn't make the feet as hot as synthetics. When buying shoes it is best to go to a shop with trained assistants, who believe in fitting shoes carefully. It is not just children who need this service. Remember that sizes often vary from one make to another – even though they shouldn't, so don't assume you are always a size 5, D fitting, for instance. If you have put on weight you could well find that you need a half size larger.

Looking after your feet

If you have the right shoes and take care of your feet, you shouldn't have too many problems.

Use a pumice stone regularly in the bath when the skin is softened to buff your feet. This will help prevent callouses forming in the first place. After-

---

RELAXATION HINTS

● Say to yourself from time to time during the day 'I am a rag doll'. It's amazing how it makes you relax, as your arms and shoulders become limp and you feel the tension drain away.

● Relax your hands. These tighten up automatically when you are tense. Shake them, pretend you are playing the piano, squeeze them hard and relax.

● If you feel that your neck is tense, let your chin drop gently on to your chest to the count of ten, then lift it to the count of two. Don't use any pressure, just let it fall naturally.

● Rotate your ankles from time to time while you are sitting down, first in one direction, then the other. People often show tension by the way they hold their feet when sitting down. Some have them sticking up unnaturally stiffly, with the whole foot

unrelaxed, others continually jog their foot up and down, particularly when sitting with legs crossed. Being aware of this is the first step to correcting it.

● Relax your face and jaw. Holding your mouth clamped shut, or grinding your teeth – both quite unconscious habits – can make your face ache, and cause headaches. I used to have this problem, and when I told a doctor that sometimes my jaw was so tight I had difficulty

speaking, he said that it was the result of an over-busy life and I would just have to live with it. Instead I eventually found my own solutions. They have to be done gently — and preferably in private! I used to do them on the thirty-mile drive into the office each day, and I'm sure I terrified some of the other drivers:

1. Open your mouth and make large chewing movements (rather like a camel!) to the count of twenty, and then relax.

2. With a slightly open mouth wiggle your chin gently from side to side. Let your jaw go loose as the movement becomes easier.

3. Whenever you feel your jaw is tight, let your mouth hang open loosely. Gently close your lips, but don't let your teeth clench together again. Your upper and lower jaw should not touch, and your tongue should loosely rest against your upper front teeth.

● If you can't sleep, or you feel you have too much on your mind, make a list. There is something magical about lists. Once you have your worries down on paper, they don't keep running through your mind in the same way. Sometimes I find it enough just ot list everything that is on my mind. Other times I go further and make lists of things to do and when. It is not just a question of being well-organized: I do it for *peace of mind*.

wards massage your feet with a rich cream.

If you have corns, don't try to deal with them yourself. Don't use medicated corn plasters or liquid corn remover: they contain a very strong dissolving acid which can cause trouble if it comes in contact with the skin. Protect the area with pressure pads and make an appointment with your chiropodist.

If you get a blister, never prick it: there's a risk of infection. Cover it with a protective plaster and leave it alone. Don't ever use hard skin scrapers or mini razor blades, a slip of the hand and you could be in trouble.

• Around the house, walk about in bare feet as much as you can. This is the best way of keeping the muscles exercised as they should be. Walking in shoes, particularly shoes with heels, is unnatural for the feet.

• To keep your feet supple, you can do this simple exercise from time to time while you are barefoot: rise up and down on your toes, four or five times. This will also strengthen the instep.

• A ten-minute soak in a foot-bath with salts provide excellent relief for tired, aching, sore feet.

• If you normally wear high heels, change into a flat pair whenever you can. If you alternate your shoes during the day your legs and feet will feel less tired. If you work, you can keep a flat pair to change into at work. At home, you can go barefoot or wear slippers.

• Have a pair of Scholl's exercise sandals. Because you have to grip with your toes to keep them on, it encourages the calf muscles to contract, thus improving the blood circulation in your legs.

• If you suffer from chilblains, do everything you can to keep your feet warm. Wear thermal socks in cold weather; wear boots with warm socks inside; take a hot water bottle to bed with you (but *don't* put your feet on it); wear bedsocks; don't toast your feet in front of the fire. Walk as much as you can to stimulate circulation.

• If you've got flat feet, you will find that wooden sandals help to strengthen

LOTTE BERK EXERCISES

Here are two of Lotte's exercises that I would recommend to all women, neither of which are difficult.

Feet
The muscles of the instep can easily shorten if you are inactive, and this can make you shuffle, rather than walk smoothly. Here is a simple exercise to avoid this.

1. With your shoes off, kneel down and sit back on your heels. Lean slightly forward; put your hands down in front of you.

 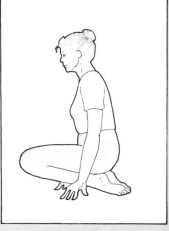

2. Now lean forward on to your hands and raise your knees off the ground. Hold this position to

the arches of your feet. It's worth asking your chiropidist if shoes built up on the inside will give you more comfort.

● If you have a tendency to get in-growing toe nails, never cut the toe nails away at the sides, or cut them too short, as this encourages them to grow inwards.

Aching Legs

What we all want to do when our legs ache is lie down and put our feet up, which is the best treatment of all. It also encourages the blood to flow back to the brain, which makes you feel refreshed.

The ideal, however, is to stop your legs hurting in the first place. Obviously if you are on your feet most of the day the most important thing is to make sure your shoes are comfortable and well-fitting, with heels that are no higher than a couple of inches. Cold weather makes the blood vessels contract which causes aching legs, and so does sitting down for long periods. You can improve the blood circulation by doing the simple ankle rotating exercise (see box on p.86).

● Wear support hose – they look like ordinary tights or stockings and can be a great comfort. They not only help varicose veins by holding them in, but they also stop your legs from becoming too tired.

You have to be more careful in the way you put them on than with ordinary tights. Sit on the bed, and ease them onto your foot and up your ankle. Inch them up your leg, pulling them quite strongly. If they are not securely pulled up when you first put them on, they will 'drag' your legs downwards, particularly the heavy duty ones, and you will feel more, rather than less, tired.

● If you suffer from varicose veins, don't sit with your legs crossed, and don't wear tight garters, otherwise the blood supply to the legs is partly cut off, making it harder for the blood to travel back up towards the heart. It is this that causes the varicose veins in the first place.

● Make sure that your nylons are not too short, as they won't stretch far enough, and you will end up with swollen and tired feet at the end of the day.

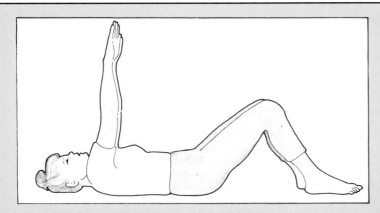

a count of three, and then sit back on your heels again. Repeat five/ten times.

As your feet become more supple, you will be able to raise your knees higher.

Spinal Stretch for an Aching Back

To cure an aching back, you need very gentle exercise, not rest. This exercise gently manipulates and moves the spine to ease aches and pains. It is perfectly safe, and can't hurt you.

1. Lie on a carpet on your back, stretch arms above your head and bend your knees.

2. Push your spine hard against the floor so that your bottom is slightly raised. Hold this position for a count of three. Relax and repeat. Do this exercise until the ache and stiffess in your back begins to ease.

• It is soothing to massage your legs from feet to knees with a little warm oil.

BODY HAIR

In my early modelling days, in the late 1940s I was booked by *Vogue* to be photographed at Stonehenge wearing beautiful, expensive evening dresses. The photographer was American, one of the great photographers of the day – his name was Coffin. Needless to say I was terrified of him. Something happened during that session that I have never forgotten. I hadn't shaved immaculately under my arms – which had to be raised continually in romantic poses. Coffin was absolutely disgusted. He told me that is was unforgivable that a woman should be so slovenly. I thought at one point that he was going to have me bundled into a car and sent back to London, and request another model instead.

Those are perhaps the best pictures I have ever had taken, and people still admire them. But whenever I look at them I remember the appalled look on Coffin's face, and how dreadful I felt.

Today, removing body hair is a matter of taste, and many younger women don't do it. But I think the majority of people still think it is unattractive not to do so. I believe that only fair-skinned women with soft blonde hair can get away with any excess hair – the rest of us must think about removing it.

No woman, for example, looks at her best with dark, hairy legs! Hairy underarms don't look nice either, especially in evening dress. Luckily, this is one of the areas where hair seems to disappear as we get older.

Legs

Shaving
The cheapest, quickest and easiest way to remove hair from your legs is to shave them. It doesn't make the hair grow back thicker and faster, as used to be believed, but it does make it feel bristly, because the ends have been blunted (think how bristly a crew-cut looks and feels on a man compared to a normal head of hair). If you do like shaving best, you might have to shave a couple of times a week depending how quickly your hair grows.

To avoid nicks and cuts you need a sharp razor and proper shaving soap. It is much more effective than ordinary soap and leaves your legs smooth. Rinse well afterwards and rub in lots of body lotion.

Depilatories
These come in cream, lotion or aerosol form, and they contain chemicals which dissolve the hair. The results are smoother and longer-lasting than shaving. However, depilatories can cause allergies, so you should make sure that you are not allergic before using them on a large area. Rub a little of the cream on a small area, such as your inner thigh, and leave for a few hours. If your skin shows no reaction, such as reddening, then you should be all right.

Depilatories work well, but the

Left: This is the famous Stonehenge photograph taken for Vogue which I feared might mark the end of my career.

BATH-TIME BEAUTY FROM THE KITCHEN

• A cup of cider vinegar in the bath is very good for dry, flaky skin.

• A cup of oatmeal will soften the water.

• A muslin bag filled with bran and placed in the bath will soften and clean the skin.

• A cup of powdered milk in the bath softens the water and your skin – and won't leave any stickiness.

• A few drops of olive or sunflower oil, together with a few drops of liquid shampoo in the bath will counteract dry skin.

• Salt makes a good exfoliating rub for the body, in the bath or shower. You can use cooking salt or Epsom salts. Rinse off well afterwards, and put on masses of body cream.

disadvantages are the unpleasant smell and the time it takes for the cream to work.

Waxing

You can have this done professionally, or buy waxing strips to use at home. Hot wax strips are laid on your legs, so that the wax melts and attaches itself to the hair. Then when it is pulled off the hair is pulled out at the root. The advantages of this method is that your skin remains soft and smooth, and because the hair is pulled out at the root, rather than cut off at surface level as with shaving, it takes longer to grow back. When it does grow back, it has a naturally pointed end, which means that it doesn't feel bristly.

The main disadvantage is that you have to let the hair grow to a certain length before it can be done efficiently. It also can hurt – though done by an experienced professional, who rips the strips off very quickly, it shouldn't.

I have to mention my own experience of waxing at home. I had to use twice the number of recommended strips before the hair came off, and even then I missed quite a lot. I never got the knack of doing it without it being painful, and I never found it easy – even though I persisted for a few months before going back to shaving.

Bleaching

If you only have a sparse growth of hair, then bleaching is a good alternative to removing it all together. Buy one of the special preparations for bleaching body hair, and follow the directions carefully.

Underarms

I would only recommend shaving, as this is a very sensitive area that is likely to become inflamed with depilatories. Also, because it is such a quick and easy process, you never have to let it get to the stubbly stage.

Use plenty of shaving cream as before, and go very carefully. Use an unperfumed cream, such as Nivea afterwards. It is best to shave your arms at night, because it is inadvisable to use anti-perspirant or deodorant on the area for at least twelve hours, as they can irritate the skin. If you do shave early in the day, rub in the Nivea, and then dust with unperfumed talc. Try not to wear anything tight-fitting under the arms (it is best not to anyway!) as this area is easily made to feel sore after shaving.

MANICURE

Tools for the Job
Small bowl of soapy water (shampoo will do) with a few drops of oil mixed in
Nail brush
Cotton wool
Oily nail varnish remover
Emery boards
Cuticle removing cream
Orange sticks
Hand lotion
Cuticle clippers
Base coat and nail polish

1. Remove old polish with cotton wool soaked in remover.

2. Shape the nails into a natural curve with the emery board. File from the side to the centre in one direction only. If you file with a sawing movement, backwards and forwards, it can split the nails and cause hang nails.

3. Rub cuticle cream into the nails with small circular movements of the thumb.

4. Soak your fingers in the water for three or four minutes. Then gently scrub them with the

Facial Hair

What was once soft and downy becomes coarser and darker on some women after the menopause. Facial hair usually appears on the upper lip, the chin and the sides of the face. Distressing as this is, you don't have to worry that you are going to grow a beard – and it is usually quite easy to deal with at home. Don't believe the people who say that face creams stimulate the growth of facial hair. Dry skin – and putting on of extra cream – occurs at much the same time as an increase in facial hair, but that doesn't mean they are connected, as many women believe.

Bleaching

This doesn't remove the hair, but it makes it far less obvious. Its main advantage is that it is quite painless, and very rarely harms the skin. It also weakens the hair, which means that it breaks off easily. When you buy a facial bleach you must follow the instructions carefully.

Shaving

If you have the smallest 'tash' at the sides of your mouth, shaving is perfectly all right. Like all methods that temporarily remove the hair, it will not affect the texture or colour of the hair, or make it grow more rapidly. This is a wide-spread misconception. That said, I know that some women would feel that the end had come if they shaved even a little hair from their faces! Also, it does feel bristly, as with legs, because of the way the hair is cut.

Plucking

This is probably one of the best ways of dealing with a few scattered hairs. Again, it has had a bad press, but as long as your skin is clean, and you take the same care as you do when plucking your eyebrows, it is a quick way of dealing with the problem. Hair does not grow back thicker and coarser if you pluck it – but it *will* grow and have to be plucked again. Don't pluck any hairs growing out of a mole. Clip these off close to the surface with a pair of nail scissors.

Waxing

This is best done in a beauty salon, as unless you are very experienced you will find it painful to do at home, and the skin may be irritated.

Depilatory cream

Most products are stringently tested

---

nail brush.

5. Using an orange stick with the blunt end covered with cotton wool, gently push the cuticle back as far as possible all round the nails, revealing the half-moon. Remove any bits of dried skin or hangnails very carefully with small cuticle clippers.

6. Clean out the nail with the pointed end of the orange stick.

7. Massage handcream into your hands, pulling the fingers as you rub in the cream, to promote good blood circulation.

Applying Polish
First apply the base coat to keep your nails from becoming discoloured and help the varnish stay on longer.

1. Start with your little finger. Draw one smooth stroke from the center of the cuticle to the tip. Then with the same action, draw a stroke on either side of the centre.

2. With a quick-drying nail polish, apply the colour in the same way. Three strokes: the first down the centre of the nail, and one on each side. Too much polish will run and smudge; too little dries too quickly. Practise makes perfect.

3. Allow to dry thoroughly, and then apply a second coat.

4. When the second coat is dry, apply a protective top coat of colourless varnish and try not to use your hands for at least half an hour. If you are in a hurry, dip your nails into iced water for a second or two, or you can buy a special spray-dry aerosol.

As I don't use coloured varnish, because I keep my nails short, I follow the manicure routine but leave out the prettiest bit!

for safety, and creams for the face are usually extra-gentle. Unless you have a super-sensitive skin they are a very good way of removing excess hair on the face, as the chemicals dissolve it away. You smooth the cream on to your face, leave for the stated time, and then wash off. It is worth doing a patch test on the back of your neck first, to make sure that you do not have an allergic reaction.

Electrolysis

If you have a real problem which you feel home remedies are not adequate to deal with, you can consider electroly-sis. Electrolysis destroys the hair at the root, so the removal is permanent. In the cases where there is some regrowth, the hair is usually much finer and weaker. Some women find it painful, and it can be expensive, and requires a great deal of time and patience, because only a few hairs can be dealt with at each session. But for some women it is the only solution. Seek advice from a trained electrolysis operator in a reputable clinic or salon. Anyone who carries out this kind of work should have a diploma from the Association of Electrolysists or the Institute of Electrolysists.

SITTING DOWN EXERCISES

This is a mini-workout for all the major joints in your body, which you can do without moving from a chair.

For Your Shoulders
Touch your right shoulder with the fingertips of your right hand. With a circular motion, move your right elbow round and round, moving from the shoulder. Repeat five times. Then repeat with the other shoulder.

For Your Elbows
Stretch your hands out in front of you with your palms upwards. Touch your shoulders with the tips of your fingers as you bend your elbows outwards. Now stretch your arms out to the side, and bring them back to your shoulders. Do this five times, getting up a rhythm as you do so.

For Your Hips
Sit on a hard chair. Grasping the back legs of the chair to keep your balance, slide your bottom forwards, keeping your shoulders against the chair back. Lift your right leg as high as you can – it doesn't have to be too high. Make five circles with your leg from the hip, then repeat with the other leg.

For Your Knees, Thighs and Buttocks
Sitting with your spine straight, bring your left knee in as close as possible to your chest, using your hands to help if necessary.

Slowly straighten your leg, so it is stretched out in front of your, before lowering it to the floor as slowly as possible. Repeat with the right leg. Do the same with each leg four more times.

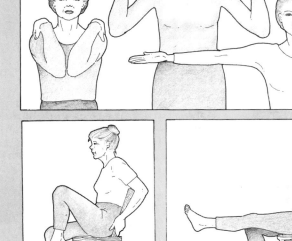

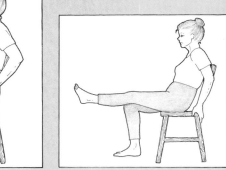

Diahann Carrol is fifty-three, the same age as Joan Collins, her rival in the TV series 'Dynasty'.

With her fabulous figure and glowing golden brown skin she can wear what most women can't – tight fitting exotic bejewelled gowns which draw attention to every line of her body. Because she is slim and has a long neck she can wear her hair quite long, but it still doesn't tumble unflatteringly over her shoulders. For day, she keeps her hair up and off her face, giving her a quieter, less obviously glamourous look.

WALKING TALL

Recently a friend of mine was telling me that her back had become so bad that she was going to an osteopath once a week. 'But the problem is,' she said, 'that the good effects of a session last such a short time – I am soon feeling as bad as ever after a day or so.' I couldn't help her from the medical angle, but it was very clear to me that her posture was making the problem worse. When sitting her body completely collapsed on itself like a concertina, and when she walked her head stuck forward and her bottom outwards, putting great strain on her spine.

I suggested giving her some deportment lessons, as I used to do in my grooming school. She was more enthusiastic than I expected, and she learnt very fast. For a month or two she popped round once a week for a lesson – and though I say it myself the effects were remarkable. Once she had mastered the correct way to stand, sit and walk, she found that her back did give her less trouble; I wish I could say that the pain ceased entirely, but it didn't! What really made the great difference in her life were the side-effects of her new deportment.

The way you hold yourself can add or subtract as much as two inches to your height. My friend literally seemed to grow, and consequently looked slimmer too. Carrying herself correctly meant that she was using muscles that hadn't been used for ages – particularly her stomach muscles – which strengthened her back and also contributed to her trim look. She refound her neck, which her previous sloppy posture had allowed to contract, and her alert sitting stance, and new walk made her look years younger.

She said that people were asking her for details of her diet, and someone accused her of having a face-lift! She was living proof of what I have always said – that good posture and deportment are more important than any other single factor in keeping you youthful-looking. And the reverse is true: bad posture ages, and also makes you look dumpier than you really are.

From the time we reach our teens, the way we walk can be a source of pleasure or intense irritation to those who know us. 'Hold your shoulders back! Don't slump! Keep your stomach in! Hold your head up!' must have been said to or by us a hundred times since we were young. But to tell some-one their deportment is bad is often taken as a personal affront. It's re-sented almost as much as if they've been told their neck is dirty when they know perfectly well it is clean!

I often wonder why the resistance is so great. Perhaps it's because the way we walk is more 'us' than anything else we do. To change the way we move our bodies is perhaps seen as an interfer-ence with the way we really are.

Unfortunately, very few of us ever actually see the way we walk and sit and stand. If we did, we'd be more co-operative. The first shock may come when we see ourselves on a home movie.

'Why didn't you tell me I walk so badly?' is the usual cry. I know that when I first saw myself on television I couldn't believe how often I slumped into my chair and how awkwardly I stood when I wasn't consciously hold-ing myself straight. I really made an effort after that. Good posture needs continual self awareness and discipline, otherwise it's too easy to slip into bad habits.

Women often first think about their posture when they put on weight. Only then do they usually make a real effort to stand up straight and pull their stomachs in. If you find it too hard going you give up and tell yourself it's all just a natural part of getting older.

Bad posture usually starts in adoles-cence. Good posture, when I was young, meant a prim 'head up, shoul-ders back, no hip waggling' which wasn't much fun and certainly didn't make me feel more attractive. I remem-ber when I was in the army during the war 'square bashing' came quite easily to me. My father had been in the army and I'd learnt to walk the military way when on a 'route' march with him and my brothers. Head back, shoulders stiff and straight, back arched, feet turned out and arms swinging briskly from the shoulder. I was the perfect sergeant major.

I started to change when I got my first modelling job at seventeen, even though I didn't have to do any actual modelling then. My straight back and level shoulders were all that was needed for fitting the clothes on me. All I had to do was stand completely still for hours, but I did get a chance to watch other models at work. With undisguised admiration I saw how gracefully they moved, and I realized then, as I do now, that the most attrac-tive and enduring thing about a woman is the way she walks. It makes the plainest woman outstanding. It lends style to the most inexpensive clothes. It radiates confidence. Make-up, figure, hair, clothes – all these things can only be presented to their best advantage by a graceful carriage. Nothing detracts more from a woman's appearance than an ungainly, unfeminine stride. You don't have to walk like a model or mince like a beauty queen, but you do need a well balanced body that is not distorted unnecessarily by awkward movements.

Just look around you. See how badly the average person walks. And yet it can be the single biggest beautifier of all.

I'm often puzzled why a carefully groomed woman who obviously cares how she looks sometimes has such an awkward gait that most of the trouble she has taken with herself is lost. Just imagine how the famous beauty would look if she came lolloping untidily down the steps of the aircraft to the whirl of the television cameras! A great deal of her glamour is dependent on the way she moves, on the confident glide, the proud position of the head, the fluid control she has over her move-ments. Watch how lightly she gets up from the chair, whatever her age. It's not something she was born with. It's a carefully studied awareness of good deportment which gives her confidence no matter how nervous and unsure she may be feeling. She knows the tricks of the trade – and I can tell you what

Right: Joan Collins. It's not just her fabulous figure and face – it's the sheer audacity of her that I love! That model girl walk – sexy, stylish confident. What a boon she is to all those who've had their fiftieth birthday and are feeling depressed about it. Keep an eye on her! She is going to set the pace for Prime Time Women for a very long time to come.

those tricks are.

They are not difficult to learn, but you have to be persistent. All the most stunning women carry themselves with a certain air. They may not be tall, beautiful or have a wonderful figure, but what they do have is an aura of confidence. Good posture shows when you are on view – entering a room for example, walking across a ballroom, coming into a theatre, coming out from the air terminal. 'I recognized her from her walk,' we often say.

When I had my Over 30's Grooming School, it was attended by a vast cross section of women. Many were housewives who spent most of their time in the company of young children, but many of them were women in responsible positions who'd hardly given a thought to themselves for years. They had one thing in common – they lacked confidence and it showed in the way they carried themselves.

Deportment gives a very clear indication of the personality. To enter a room, head down, shoulders hunched, is an obvious sign of nervousness and timidity. So is standing awkwardly, shifting from one foot to another, or continually twisting your hands. Shyness, arrogance, depression, joy – all these are expressed in body language. Excitement will make you move with greater speed, while fear makes you drag your feet.

The aim in improving your deportment is not to wipe out natural mannerisms. If you watch models at a fashion show they all have (or should have!) beautiful carriage, gliding effortlessly along the catwalk. But they will be quite different in the way they present themselves and respond to the clothes they are wearing. If they are wearing something they hate, you'd never realize it. Most women, if they are wearing something that doesn't make them feel good, feel like hiding in a corner. But when you know how to walk well you can make *everything* look good.

POSTURE

The first thing to get right is your posture, and for this you need a full-length mirror. Bad posture is a habit that has come to feel normal, so you have to *see* what you look like, rather than attempting to make changes without looking at what it is you are doing wrong.

Place the mirror where you can see yourself walking as well as standing: don't have it tipped at an angle otherwise you'll get a distorted view.

Practise your standing positions in front of the mirror. Once you have moved yourself into the correct position, make a note of how it *feels*, so that even when the mirror is not there you have a good idea what you should be doing to keep yourself looking poised and relaxed. Remember how you look when you're standing well; if there is a great difference between that and your usual posutre keep that image clearly in your mind so that you are never tempted to let yourself go.

What good posture can give you is a better figure; watch yourself as you stand correctly and you will notice the improvement instantly.

The hidden benefit of correct posture is that it ultimately influences your body shape, because it strengthens and firms the supportive muscles. Your body can either improve or deteriorate according to your posture. That is why posture affects both health and beauty.

Now to begin: Stand with your back to the mirror and then turn slowly. Make no attempt to stand 'properly' at this stage; move and stand exactly as you usually do. The important thing now is to get a realistic idea of how you usually hold yourself. Take a good look at your stance from front and side. Can you see room for improvement? Common faults are rounded shoulders and the slight hump at the back of the neck. Also you may notice your head poked forward or thrown back, and a protruding stomach: All

Left: This is the way to wear glasses – as a stunning accessory. Sophia Loren, in her early fifties, knows all about looking good. First of all, the way she walks – the most endurably attractive thing about a woman – with her head held high and that famous wide smile. Her Italian understated chic, and the clever scarf at the neckline which hides any imperfections but at the same time gives a pretty frame to the face.

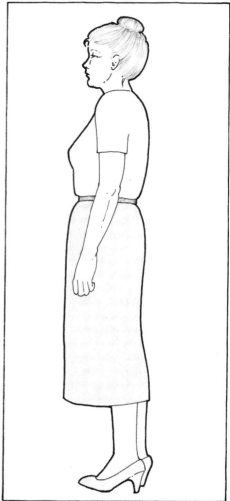

these things can be corrected.

● Imagine that you are very tall and broad shouldered and that you have a cord running through the whole length of your body which is lifting and stretching you upwards. Feel the cord tugging at the crown of your head, drawing your head up and lengthening your neck.

● Keep your head high: with your chin tucked in and your eyes level you will not be able to throw your head backwards, a position that is responsible for many headaches and shoulder pains.

● Lift your shoulders high into a shrug, then roll them upwards and backwards. Relax them, and your body will fall into a comfortable position. Think of your shoulders broadening, stretching out sideways, so that they don't come forwards or pull back unnaturally tightly, or raise themselves round your ears.

● Tell yourself that your hands are heavy. Your arms should fall loosely to your sides with your fingers lightly curled under. Alternatively, place your arms in front of you with the fingers loosely linked.

• Clench your buttocks together gently. At the same time you will feel your stomach muscles tightening and your pelvis tilting forward. At this angle, the pelvis, which is a basin, contains the stomach. When your buttocks are totally relaxed, or your bottom is sticking out, then your pelvis tips your stomach out of the basin, making it look bigger than it really is. In this position, the muscles that are supposed to hold the base of your spine are made to work properly, which strengthens your lower back.

• Now think about your legs. Your legs should be slightly apart. Are your knees in a locked position? This is very common and can make you feel quickly tired when you are standing. Tell yourself to relax your knees. When they are very slightly bent, you will find standing even more comfortable.

• See that your feet are turned slightly outwards: imagine the outer part of the foot taking your weight.
Your body should now be correctly balanced. Can you see the difference? If this feels unnatural to begin with, it will soon start to feel normal if you practise it regularly. By consciously concentrating on your posture you will not only get into the habit of standing well, but it will continue to improve. A 'dowager's hump', for instance, is caused by muscles shortening in your shoulders and neck area. If you continue to think about your shoulders broadening, the muscles will slowly lengthen and the hump will eventually be ironed out.

STANDING

It is one thing learning to get your posture right for a few minutes in front of the mirror, but you may feel that you will never be able to keep it up for any length of time – at a party or the bus stop for instance. Slouching, with your arms crossed and your weight heavily on one leg is a very common way of coping with having to stand for more than a few minutes at a time – but although you may *believe* this feels comfortable, it actually contributes to your feeling tired. Standing well not only looks more attractive, it is also easier once you get the hang of it.

• Having ensured that your posture is good, step forward slightly with one foot. Your back leg should be straight and the front one slightly bent. Rock slightly in this position, until you can feel that your weight is equally balanced between your two feet. It is when you are taking the weight on one leg alone that you tend to feel tired and have to shift about from foot to foot. When the weight is equally balanced you are much more likely to retain that still, poised look, that catches the eye.

• An alternative is to stand in the basic posture, with your feet slightly apart, and turned out very slightly. Again, it is important to check that your weight is evenly balanced between both feet. This is a slightly less elegant pose, but particularly good when standing for long periods at a time. This is proved by the fact that it is the position favoured by the Royal Family who, as a matter of routine, have to stand for much longer periods than most of us are used to.

WALKING

How do you walk? It is something we usually give little thought to. For that reason many women's posture goes to pieces when it comes to moving anywhere. Once you start thinking about it, walking can become a complicated business, almost a new experience, so that what was once spontaneous becomes something very different. Very few people walk well, and there's a world of difference between an elegant walk and a walk that's just average.
    The very word 'deportment' makes

most people yawn. It has such a dreary, spartan image and yet it was one of the favourite lessons in my grooming school. The older women particularly liked it. After they'd learnt about make-up and hairstyling, exercise and diet, they were raring to get on the catwalk. They wanted all the grace and confidence they could get to go with their new image. Most of them hadn't the slightest idea what was wrong with the way they walked, but they felt fairly certain it wasn't right!

It's amazing just how quickly you can change a lifetime of bad habits once you put your mind to it. At first it can feel strange. For instance, if you've been used to turning your feet inwards, it's quite difficult to point them straight ahead, let alone point them slightly outwards. If you've always shuffled along, then walking from the hips with the pelvis tilted forward is not easy, either.

It takes time to learn how to walk correctly naturally, without having to think about it all the time, but once you do, the rewards are so great that it's worth the effort. Here, step-by-step, is the right way.

1. Always start by making sure that your posture is correct. Repeat the

---

GOOD posture
- makes you look slimmer
- makes you look younger
- makes you look taller
- makes you feel less tired
- allows your internal organs to work properly

BAD posture
- weakens your back, neck and stomach muscles – gives you aches and pains
- makes your breasts sag
- thickens the waistline
- encourages tension
- gives you indigestion, constipation and poor circulation
- encourages a double chin and a dowager's hump
- makes your chest concave

---

various stages until you are standing tall and broad and well-balanced.

2. Keeping the upper part of your body still, move from the hips, your bottom slightly pushed forwards, taking fairly long strides.

When I was taught to walk this way in my first real modelling job with Spectator Sports in London, I had to practise with my hands on my bottom, pushing first one cheek forward and then the other! It feels (and looks) rather silly but it's a good way to learn and you very quickly get a nice gliding movement. Imagine, also, that your legs are very long, reaching right up under your arms. and as you move, tread lightly, keeping your feet slightly turned out. Walking this way from the hips gives you a swing, and it makes you use the whole length of your leg. If you walk from the knee, which many women do, you'll have tiny mincing steps. It will also make you bounce up and down and make it more difficult to hold yourself really straight.

3. Hold your head high, with your chin tucked in and your eyes level. Think of yourself leading with your forehead. Your shoulders should be straight and relaxed. Remember to think of them broadening as you walk. Let your arms hang loosely, with a slight, natural swing. Your fingers should only be lightly curled under and brushing the side of your skirt as you move.

4. Hold your tummy in lightly: if you pull the muscles too strongly you may pull your chest downwards.

It's really just as simple as that. Watch yourself, when you can, in shop windows. They may not be very flattering to the face, but they will give you a pretty accurate impression of how you are walking. I often pull myself up an extra inch whenever I catch sight of myself in shop windows.

Even if you don't get the hang of walking like this instantly you should try to become aware of your own way of walking. There are some common faults which you might find that you share. Learning to stop these habits will help you towards a beautiful glide.

• Do you swing your arms? It is common to see women swinging their arms about like a windmill. It doesn't help you move along any faster, but it does look ungainly. It is hard to maintain a smooth walk unless your arms are falling loosely at your sides, just swinging slightly with the motion of the walk. If this is one of your problems, try this exercise every now and again: clench your fists and punch your arms downwards, until they are stretched straight. Now let go. Feel the heaviness in your arms, and the relaxed muscles. Swinging requires muscular effort. Aim for the relaxed feel.

• Do you turn your feet in? Pigeon-toed walking can make you look bandy, and rather mincing. Glance down frequently at your feet, and make conscious efforts to turn them outwards. Think of your knees turning outwards, and pointing away from each other: it is harder to turn your feet in if the knees are turned out. Keep remembering that the weight of your body must be distributed along the outer edge of your feet.

• Do you tend to lean forward when you walk, with your bottom stuck out? First of all, slow down. This kind of walk tends to be developed because you think it makes you walk faster. In fact, it impedes your progress, because you can't get a long stride with your body jutting forward. Bringing yourself back to the tall, correct posture and moving from the hips is faster as well as more elegant.

• Do you throw your head back? This is common amongst women who are trying to stand up straight. Rather than thinking of the crown of the head rising upwards, they raise their foreheads and the head goes back. This is very tiring for the neck and shoulder muscles, and it encourages a dowager's hump. Catch yourself when you are doing this, and tuck your chin in slightly. Think of your head separating from your shoulders and your neck lengthening.

• Do you walk with your hands in your pockets and your shoulders slumped? This is one of the least attractive and most ageing of postures. Always take your hands out of your pockets when you catch yourself doing this: otherwise you will not be able to straighten your shoulders so easily. Breathe in slowly and very deeply. As your chest expands, your shoulders should start to roll backwards. Bring your head up high as you do this. Keep your chest in a high position, and think of your shoulders broadening.

• Do you walk with your elbows stuck out, or keep your arms stiff with clenched fists? Loosely hanging arms are essential to an elegant walk. When you notice your elbows or your arms stiff, shake your hands briskly downwards three or four times as if you have something stuck to them that you are trying to get off. The last time you do this, hold them stiffly straight, with your fingers spread out for a moment, then let them relax. Try to keep them relaxed.

• Do you shuffle along with small steps? This scurrying is the opposite of elegant. Try to get yourself out of the habit by counting your strides. Walk for a few minutes saying 'one and two and one and two' etc until you have developed a new rhythm. On 'one' you put the first foot down. Don't put the other foot down until you say 'two'.

If you are seriously interested in improving your deportment you'll find practising great fun. Combine it with walking for exercise and you'll have the added bonus of your clothes looking

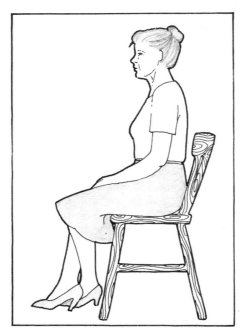 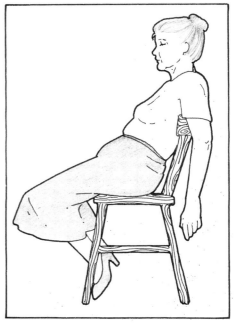

better on you because your figure will improve.

THE SECRET OF GOOD GROOMING

It is a pity that there aren't deportment and grooming schools specifically for older women any more. There are schools for young girls – but obviously they are not suitable. The two age groups are miles apart – general grooming, presentation and deportment have to be much more sophisticated as you get older. You can't get away with being badly groomed or looking as if you lack confidence.

We're lucky that our generation had such good examples to follow. Models, actresses and fashionable women in the public eye exuded elegance, and most of us have not forgotten the things we learnt then. But it's been a long time since elegance or grooming has been considered in any way desirable.

Things are beginning to change now, I am delighted to say. A report published recently in *The Sunday Times* on the 1986 London Fashion Week, which

was attended by over nine thousand buyers from overseas, was very sobering.

It said, '. . . Even the most dedicated followers of British fashion were to be seen, sunk low in their chairs, their eyes shaded with embarrassment. . .it sounds unkind, cruel even, to say that they [the young designers] deserve to fail. But fail they should when they haven't even learned to use a steam iron, let alone an overlocker; when hems trail and threads dangle.'

It has taken a long, long time for the tide to change. I have often felt a lone voice in my praise and admiration of the older woman with her sense of – to use an old-fashioned but apt word – decorum. In the face of everything freakish and tatty, and at the risk of being called old-fashioned and dull, she has continued to keep up the standards of good grooming even though she may have fallen considerably behind with 'fashion'.

I can always spot an ex-model by the way she moves. Even if – which is unlikely! – she has doubled in size, she'd still be recognizable. Apart from her general poise she has certain tricks that add up to a nonchalant elegance. If you have ever earned your living modelling clothes you don't forget those tricks in a hurry. They are an asset whatever you are doing – at work, as well as in your social and everyday life.

You'd never see a trained model, for example, with a handbag held in front of her, sitting on a protruding stomach like a shelf, or hugging a coat awkwardly over her arm. Everything is worn with an unobtrusive style – so unobtrusive in fact that the uninitiated don't really know what it is about her that makes her so different.

Those are the tricks I am going to tell you now. You already know about posture, standing and walking. Now for that other major pitfall – sitting.

Sitting Pretty

The biggest laugh I ever get at my shows is when I demonstrate how badly some women sit. I sit on a chair on the stage with my legs wide apart, round shouldered and with my arms folded across my chest. An everyday sight – one we see regularly when we're on the bus, or in a waiting room, or walking past the benches in the park. And yet it always brings the house down, and many of those who are laughing the loudest are sitting in front of me in exactly that position!

It is only difficult if you are very overweight to get your thighs close together, but even then it's perfectly possible to keep your feet crossed at the ankles so that stocking tops and pants aren't on view. It's the legs wide apart that I find unforgivable, and looks so ugly.

There is a new generation of women who sit badly. Many of them have literally grown up in trousers and have only fairly recently taken to wearing skirts. For about twenty years legs practically disappeared from view and 'sitting pretty' in trousers wasn't so important. Trousers are worn in a much more relaxed, casual way. You can't really look clumsy – or show your knickers – in them and you can adopt positions that would look ludicrous, or lewd, if you were wearing a dress.

But slumping is not connected only to the clothes you wear. Sitting in a slouched position encourages spare tyres, large stomachs, double chins and indigestion! In fact, more double chins and sagging jaw lines are acquired sitting round-shouldered while watching TV, knitting, or typing than by being overweight. It is one of the quickest ways of helping your figure to deteriorate.

If you're not used to sitting with a straight back it *feels* rather prim and unrelaxed when you first hold yourself in that position, but it *looks* a thousand times better immediately. Just think of television announcers, both men and women. None of them slump – they'd hardly be in that kind of job if they did – but they look perfectly relaxed.

Sitting correctly starts with sitting down. If you happen to be at a formal meeting where you have to walk to your seat in view of an audience, you might as well do it elegantly.

This is the method we taught in our school. Learning to sit down like this takes a bit of practice. Don't attempt it in public until you are quite sure that you have mastered it.

• Go up to the chair, turn your back on it and feel the edge of the seat with your calf. Without looking behind you, smooth the back of your skirt at the same moment as you sit down, to stop the skirt from creasing.

What you *don't* do is grab the back of the chair and drag it towards you. That scraping noise is a familiar sound in a large hall, because everybody is doing just that! Neither do you stand up in front of the chair and the audience, and smooth the back of your skirt with both hands *before* starting to sit down.

• Sit with the base of your spine

touching the back of the chair. In this position you'll find it very difficult, if not impossible, to slump. Let your body relax as your spine remains straight. It is surprisingly comfortable – you can sit or drive for long stretches of time without your back getting tired. As a bonus, your internal organs will be in their right position which will allow them to function properly!

● Here are four positions for your legs.
1. Place them together in front of you with your knees together and both feet on the floor (not sticking straight out resting on your heels. This is the classic 'trip up' position).
2. Cross your legs at the ankles.
3. Slant your legs to one side with one leg slightly behind the other.
4. Cross your legs above the knee, slanting them to one side, with one leg placed by the side of the other. This is not a very comfortable position but it's a very good way to show off beautiful legs!

Rest your hands lightly in your lap, or,

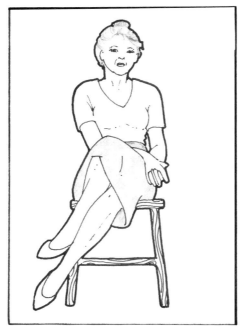

if you cross your legs, place them against the opposite thigh so that you are well balanced.

Positions to avoid:

● Don't draw up your knees and rest on your toes.

● Don't cross your leg above the knee for any length of time if you have a tendency to varicose veins.

● Don't draw your heels back under the chair with your ankles crossed.

● Don't twist your legs round the legs of chairs.

● Don't sit with your legs crossed shaking one foot ferociously – you will look supremely unrelaxed!

When rising from a chair, do it as lightly as possible. Don't heave yourself up by pressing on to the arms or seat. Few people really need to do this, and it is the best way of making yourself look old and decrepit. Don't slide off the chair sideways, either.

Here is the correct way:
1. Uncross your legs or feet.
2. Draw your feet under the chair, keeping your knees together.
3. Move the top half of your body forward over your feet, then stand up and step forward.

If you are tucked right back in a deep armchair it's much more difficult to get up, of course, and the only way to manage *is* to slide forward and ease yourself up using the arms of the chair. Outside of my own home I try to avoid them, especially if I'm wearing a tight skirt. I once got stuck in one and had to be helped out by a very gallant, but not particularly strong, young man. He had an awful struggle and nearly ended up in my lap. It was made worse by my host asking if I was feeling all right and I'm sure everyone thought I'd had too much wine to drink. I'm very careful not to let anything like that happen again!

Getting out of a car is a special case, as it can be very awkward, particularly if the car is low and sporty. The important thing to remember is not to get out head first, or you will have a terrible struggle. Swing your legs out of the car first and then ease the rest of your body out.

Similarly, **getting into a car** can be tricky if you try to climb in with your feet first. What you should do is bend at the knees, settle your bottom in first, and then swing your feet in afterwards.

Bending Down

Even picking something up from the floor has its right way. We know how ugly it can look done the wrong way, and I'm quite sure we've all had a good view of underwear and goodness knows what when somebody has bent over from the waist to pick something up. You may think that it is a good exercise for the waistline, but it is very bad for your back, as well as being ungainly.

This is how to do it:

● Bend down from the knees, not from the waist, with one foot slightly in front of the other and your bottom tucked in, keeping your back straight – like a very low curtsey. If you are lifting something heavy, hold it close to your body so that your thighs and back carry the strain.

Wearing your clothes the right way

It's the little things that often spoil the picture. The clumsy bag with the pretty evening dress; the strappy sandals with the classic suit; the daytime cardigan over a theatre dress. But even when you've got everything right, the *way* you wear your clothes can make or mar the final impression.

Let us start with the handbag.

The Classic Bag

The wrong way to carry it:
Look at a photograph of a group of women taken on a holiday outing or at a convention. At least half of them have their arm stuck through their bag so that it sits on the stomach, while their fists are raised rather menacingly in front. They carry the handbag on their right arm, which makes shaking hands or holding a cup of tea a real problem. It looks clumsy and it spoils the line of the dress.

If you are not holding your bag this way you are probably holding it by the handles, hanging down Minnie Mouse fashion. I know this is the popular way, but it always looks rather prim to me, and you won't find a really elegant woman carrying her bag like that.

The right way:
Slip your left arm through the handle of your handbag from left to right so that it sits on the side of your hip. This leaves your right hand free, and the bag never swings awkwardly round to the front. If you are left-handed, you reverse the procedure, of course.

The Shoulder Bag

I love shoulder bags, especially slim ones with slender straps, and I always wear them during the day. They look uncluttered and leave the hands free, and I think they're much less stodgy than the conventional classic. They *don't* look good, though, if they're bulging at the seams. If you feel obliged to carry around a lot of things, then a classic bag is best. But even shoulder bags have to be worn in a certain way.

The wrong way to carry it:
Don't hang on to the bag, pulling your shoulder downwards as you do so. This throws the hips as well as the shoulders out of alignment. Schoolgirls who carry their satchels in this way are invariably lopsided and it's one of the biggest contributions to bad deportment throughout their lives.

The right way:
To prevent your shoulder bag slipping,

hold the strap lightly just below shoulder level. In this way you can't drag your shoulder down and your body will remain straight.

The Clutch Bag

The wrong way to carry it:
Don't tuck it under your arm. You'll have to adopt an awkward position to keep it in place and it's a perfect target for a bag snatcher.
The right way:
Hold it in your hand, pressed against your side, or tip it so that it slants forwards and outwards.

Taking off a coat

Always take your time when taking off your coat, particularly if you are in a restaurant and the waiter is hovering around waiting for it. It's when you're rushed that it looks clumsy. Sleeves get caught up, often ending up inside out, and to make matters worse someone usually tries to drag it off your shoulders.

Decline help (it is different when you are putting the coat on). Remove your gloves slowly, put them next to your handbag and — take your time.

● If you have buttons, start unbuttoning from the bottom upwards.

● Holding the lapels, push the coat backwards and let it slip down to wrist level where you can catch it and drape it over one arm. Then either hang it up or hand it to someone else to do so. It takes a bit of practice but it's worth it.

● When putting on your coat always hold it by the lapel to ease your arms in. If you have buttons, do them up from the *top* downwards.

Gloves

Gloves are back in fashion for the first time in many years, but this time round they're very expensive, especially good leather ones. Like a hat, they undoubtedly put the finishing touch to an outfit, as well as protecting our hands at the same time. Hands don't age half as quickly if they're kept covered up.

In my early modelling days the way we put on and took off gloves was an important part of our job and I used to love to watch Barbara Goalen during a fashion show. She did it with such aplomb that it's no wonder that models were considered the epitome of elegance.

I remember showing a friend of mine how to look after her expensive leather gloves. I saw her dragging them on so that the seams would split; when she took them off she pulled the cuffs over her fingers, often leaving them inside out. She was intrigued to know that she was doing something wrong. She couldn't imagine there was a 'right' way to do such a simple thing as putting on and taking off a pair of gloves.

● Holding the hand upwards with the palm facing, smooth the glove on, one finger at a time, starting with the little finger, then stroke the cuff into position.

● To remove, they should be inched off slowly, starting with the little finger and ending with the thumb. When the fingers have been eased free, it is a simple matter to pull the entire glove off by holding the empty fingers.

● When carrying the gloves, hold them together so that the fingers all lie in the same direction.

Umbrellas

Many women these days choose a collapsible umbrella. They're easy to carry, are often small enough to go in the handbag and they certainly don't get lost so easily. But the more solid umbrellas are still a blessing when it is windy as well as rainy and plenty of people still use them. The problem is that they are dangerous — those with lethal steel spikes have done untold damage ever since they were invented.

Right: Dinah Shore. Unbelievably in her seventies, the American singer wisely chooses the simplest of casual classics with a shirt cut low at the neck to give a longer line to the body. Everything about her is relaxed, from the unbuttoned jacket, pushed up sleeves to the shoulder bag (which she is holding correctly by the strap and not leaning on heavily for support) and the simple hair-style. The temptation is to dress up this kind of outfit thus losing the very essence of its success — simplicity.

The Queen Mother, showing perfectly how to wear a stole, carry a handbag and long gloves, and shake hands at the same time.

Most of them nowadays are carried by men, usually stuck over their shoulder or thrashed about wildly as they walk. I have no way of appealing to them to be more careful, but the rest of us *can* do something about it.

● If you are carrying an umbrella and a handbag this is the way to do it so that there's no danger of poking someone's eye out. Hang your bag over your wrist. Grasp the stem of the umbrella and hold it between the first and middle fingers. Let your handbag slip over your hand and catch it with the other fingers. Hold it together with the umbrella. The brolly should now hang safely by your side, sword fashion, protected by your handbag.

Wearing a stole
These are endlessly useful, not only for keeping warm, but as a stylish fashion accessory. They make the perfect evening wrap or a good alternative to a cardigan over a summer dress. They also suit most women. But to be worn stylishly they shouldn't be hugged tightly around the body as if you're standing in a gale. A stole should DRAPE the shoulders so the dress underneath can be seen. If you need your hands to be free, anchor it on one shoulder with a brooch or, if it is long enough and not too bulky, toss both ends back over your shoulder.

MAKING AN ENTRANCE

Entering a crowded room, convinced all eyes are on you, daunts just about everyone. I know from experience that it doesn't necessarily help if your face and hair are looking great or if you're wearing something that really suits you. That's where good deportment comes in, it gives you the confidence to make an entrace with presence.

Even outwardly confident women often feel unsure of themselves but the difference is they know how to put on a good act! They don't fidget or fumble, they stand tall and look around them with an air of pleasant expectancy. They are uncluttered. If they've arrived with parcels or a coat they are not in evidence. They keep one hand free in case they have to shake hands. They look, in fact, cool, calm and collected.

Before I knew how, I would stand outside the door, take a deep breath, then throw back my head and stride in forcefully. It certainly got me into the room, if somewhat gustily, but once inside most of the embarrassment returned. I often wished I could have continued to walk through the room and out of the door at the other end!

It is even worse if you don't know anybody. I had to learn the hard way because I attended a lot of functions on my own, but the most important thing I discovered is that everyone loves to talk to *somebody*. You don't have to make clever conversation: just a comment about the event, the weather (never a boring subject to us!); how many people in the room you know or don't know etc. I've never met anyone who hasn't been grateful not to be left standing in silence.

Now when I have to make an entrance, I still take a deep breath, but I don't stride in forcefully any more. I come in slowly, stand still for a few seconds and look around the room. This gives me time to take in the scene and allows anyone who knows me to come over and say hello. If that doesn't happen I move casually around the room as if I expect to see someone I know (which I hopefully do!) with a smile ready for anyone who looks friendly. If there is a buffet I get myself a drink and something to eat and move to the nearest circle of people. It is comparatively easy then to get into conversation with someone and eating has the advantage of giving you something to do with your hands.

If you are with a partner then of course it is that much easier. Even so, I've known plenty of women who look absolutely gorgeous and yet scuttle in like a scared mouse. They hang on to the man like grim death, or stand behind him. What they should do, of course, is rest their hand lightly on his arm, and stand as equals next to him.

GOING UP AND DOWN A STAIRCASE IN A LONG DRESS

This can be quite a tricky business and I've seen it done in a number of most inelegant ways!

The main thing to remember is not to pick up both sides of your dress and hold it *out to the side* as children do when wearing a party frock.

If you want to hold the banister rail as you go up, take hold of one side of your dress with your free hand and pull it towards the front, holding it up so that it clears the step.

If you are not holding the rail, use both hands to lift the sides of the dress, bringing all the fullness to the front as you lift it.

Make sure that the bag you are carrying can be linked over your wrist when you do this. I always take one that has a small chain handle, and I tuck it back inside the bag when I want to use it as a clutch.

As you go up the stairs don't put the whole of your foot on the step, just the ball. If you use the whole of your foot you will find it makes you lurch forward as you lift the full weight of your body. This will always make you look as if you are struggling to get up, even if you could bound up two stairs at a time! The only time you should put the whole of your foot firmly on each step is when you are unsteady on your feet.

Coming down the stairs, hold your dress in the same way, but this time *do* place the whole of your foot on the stair, pointing your feel slightly sideways as you do so.

PUBLIC SPEAKING

Most of us sooner or later find that we have to stand up and give a speech. It can be just a few words of welcome or considerably longer. It can be informal, such as at a wedding or anniversary, or more formal if we belong to a group such as a woman's club or a political or community organization. Whichever it is, speaking in public can be a terrifying experience, and full of pitfalls.

Regular speaking at women's luncheon clubs has taught me some valuable lessons. I am by no means a conventional speaker, but there are certain things common to all speakers.

• Know what you are going to say. Have your introduction and ending properly worked out, and try not to rely too heavily on your notes. Even the best speech, if it is read rather than spoken, falls flat.

• Don't go over your allotted time. Remember to count in the time for questions, if they are appropriate. It can be worth 'planting' a question with a member of the audience, to break the ice quickly.

• Try to sound as good as you look. Voices can be very ageing; even if you are feeling very tired and strung up make an effort to keep your voice light and flexible. The more energy you put into your voice the more energy it will put into your listeners.

Entering the room
• If you have to enter the room where people are waiting for you, don't turn your back on them as you close the door. All eyes will be on you, and your entrance is important. As you come through the door, step to one side and shut it by stretching out a hand behind you while you are still facing the room.

Posture
• Always remember your posture. You cannot project your voice properly if your body is slumped. Stand tall, with our stomach held in and your weight evenly balanced on the balls of your feet.

• If your feet are too close together you will sway backwards and forwards. If they are too far apart you will sway from side to side to maintain your balance.

• Look around at your audience and don't be afraid to smile. Giving a talk doesn't have to be a sober affair.

• Beware of distracting mannerisms. You may not be aware of them yourself, so this is where you need a good friend to point them out to you. The most common ones are fussing with hair or a necklace; taking glasses on and off; pulling your earlobe, or the side of your face; fiddling with the front of your dress.

Your clothes
If you are confident that you look good, you won't feel so nervous. It is important to dress to suit the occasion.

• Tailored clothes are always right, and can look different if they are highlighted with a stylish hat or scarf.

• Anything too eye-catching mesmerizes the audience and often distracts their attention. So don't wear startlingly bright colours, or a hat with trimmings that move when you talk, such as feathers. Don't wear jewellery that dangles, either, or anything too glittery that catches the light.

• An unusual prop, such as pince-nez (which many speakers use because they find them more convenient than glasses) are also distracting.

DRESSING WITH STYLE

Almost everything we read about clothes talks about fashion, and I believe that if you want to look good, then this emphasis is wrong.

Anyone can look at a magazine picture, buy all the items featured and dress herself up to look like the model – and then wonder what on earth went wrong. You'll be in the height of fashion, of course, but your style rating will be nil. And you won't look anywhere near your best.

Style is individual and elusive, and we all develop our own particular look. But it needn't be a serious business getting everything right. I break my own rules all the time. If I fall in love with a particular outfit or a pair of shoes I am likely to buy it, even if it is totally unsuitable and I would advise my best friend against it! A strict clinical approach has a lack of spontaneity – and fun. I believe that every woman, given the confidence, and allowing herself the 'right' to spend time on herself

can develop a style that makes her look good, and gives her a real sense of enjoyment.

But I know that many women have lost confidence, or are utterly bewildered by the fashion magazines. They simply don't know what to wear, and feel that if they can't keep up with fashion then they might as well stop trying. As Elaine Stritch, the stylish American actress, remarked, 'I adore to see women well-dressed and it makes me sick to see someone attractive with the wrong things on. Getting everything together makes life more fun, gives you a lovely posh feeling and it makes cities prettier!'

So in this chapter I plan to give you some pointers from my own experience. These will help you plan a basic wardrobe, give you ideas about how to make sure you look your best in your clothes, old and new – and give you some model's and couturier's tips on how to accentuate your good points and camouflage any problem areas.

Gertrude Shilling. What an appetite she has for life! How she loves to stand out in a crowd and not blend unobtrusively into the background! The sheer pleasure she gets from wearing her son's extraordinary and often eccentric hats at Ascot always gets noticed by the press. The fashion editor of the Observer wrote recently, 'Of all the women who dress for Ascot Mrs Shilling seems ultimately to be the only one who really makes a go of it.'

'An outfit's not complete without a hat,' she says, 'Women often say they'd like to have the nerve to look like me. Well, I tell them, all you have to do is make the effort.'

MAKING FASHION WORK FOR US

I love the fashion world. It has been a most important part of my life for a long time, and I am always interested in what is new. But I know that a lot of women feel tyrannized and intimidated by the extremes of fashion to the point that they give up. The trick is to spot the fashion themes that underpin the extremes, to notice the colours that are being used and to pick out the elements that would suit *you*.

Women right at the hub of beauty and fashion are never slaves to what is 'in' or 'out', but stick to an individual style that suits them. As Coco Chanel remarked, 'Fashion is that thing which is soon out of fashion.'

Estee Lauder says she goes to the couture collections each year to 'get a hint of the newest fashions so that I can adapt last year's clothes accordingly'. Jean Muir, designer of wonderful clothes that are admired and coveted by women the world over, dresses entirely in navy — just the style and shape changing according to the fashion. The simplicity and economy, she says, suits her style, personality and sense of order.

If you are going to make fashion work for you, the first thing you must do is look at what is on offer — but look critically.

You don't have to give more than a fleeting glance at some of the crazy fashions you see in the street, but it's just as well to be aware of them because it helps you to define more clearly how you *don't* want to look.

Extremes in fashion usually pass quickly and the high street shops bulge with copies of the idiosyncratic outfits the designers dream up, only to change their stock completely within months.

Fashion writers, too, are in the business of creating *news*. There is nothing newsworthy in a flattering well-cut classic outfit: they mainly want sensational items to feature. Fashion stories such as TEAM UP HIS OVERSIZE EVENING SHIRT WITH YOUR LEATHER MINI and THE CITY BOWLER GIVES YOU CITY CHIC or BUY POTS OF BRIGHT LIME AND ORANGE DYE AND PAINT YOUR GYM SHOES FOR HIGH FASHION COLOUR and KNOT YOUR THICK COTTON TIGHTS INTO A CRAZY LITTLE HAT are harmless good fun, but nothing to do with *us*.

However you can learn lots of useful things from magazines and window-shopping. I always try to have a good look before I buy anything. You can see which colours are in, and how they are co-ordinated and accessorized. You can pick up good ideas like this, and if a particular new colour appeals to you then you can incorporate it in what you wear.

You don't need a whole new outfit to look up-to-date: a touch of colour in the latest shade is often enough — a hat or scarf, or maybe gloves. It's one of the quickest and cheapest ways of looking fashionable, and it's much smarter to have just a touch of scarlet, royal blue, tartan — or whatever is currently dominating the scene — than to be covered in it from head-to-toe.

The other things you can pick up are the small style details that show that you are aware of what is fashionable. Are belts narrow or wide? Are shoes flat, high, or broguey? Are jackets shorter or longer, lapels wide or slim? Are stockings inconspicuous or jazzy? Are buttons brassy and bold or toning? Are trouser legs tapering or baggy? Changing some of these details can up-date your whole look. A good example over the last couple of years is the broad-shouldered look. Dresses, shirts and even cardigans, can be given a fashionable life by adding shoulder pads. You can remove them when the fashion finally passes.

There is another kind of inspiration you can get from magazines, newspapers and television. There are bound to be women in the public eye you identify with and, unlike models, they come in all ages. You can pick up fashion tips from them. You'll notice that most of them look good and stylish, and while they are fashionable they don't go over the top. Seeing how they adapt today's look can give you some very good ideas.

The most elegant women, whatever their age, usually have a very simple approach to the clothes they wear. They like well-cut, classically styled clothes in beautiful fabrics. That is a very good guideline for the rest of us. Whether you have a lot of money or a little, buy the very best you can afford. It's far better to have a few good items than a cupboard full of rubbish. Some of our chain stores, particularly Marks and Spencer, of course, sell excellent clothes at very reasonable prices. Watch out for sizing though: you may need to buy a size larger than normal as they are not cut particularly generously.

PLANNING YOUR WARDROBE

We all moan 'I haven't a thing to wear!' knowing full well that we have lots of clothes. What we mean is that we don't like them any more, and are not sure if anything goes together. It's easy to say 'If I had lots of money I'd know exactly what to wear'. But rushing out and buying new things doesn't solve the problem.

The good news is that you don't need a lot of money to get a working wardrobe together, although I'd be the first to agree that it's a great help! It takes planning, patience, confidence, know-how and time. As Sophia Loren said in her autobiography, 'Style is adapting what you can afford to buy and turning it into something special.'

If that sounds daunting, don't be put off. You can take it one step at a time. The first thing to do is to sort through your clothes and decide what to keep.

Just go through this season's clothes first: you can leave the rest for a few months. To attempt to do everything at one go is far too exhausting and enough to put you off the job altogether.

BE RUTHLESS

Grit your teeth and get rid of the things you never wear, no matter how much they cost. They're doing nobody any good just hanging in your wardrobe – except perhaps the moths. If they're too good to throw away, the charity shops will be only too happy to have them – but don't forget your younger female relatives either. Even if they think that you and your clothes are old-fashioned, 'antiques' are another matter! Just think how popular 'grandad' vests were recently, worn instead of a T-shirt.

I wasn't always organized about my wardrobe, by any means. I used to buy clothes on impulse and it was chaotic trying to work out what to wear with what. There was always plenty to choose from but never the *right* thing, and I wasted money on clothes I rarely wore because they didn't go with anything else or were quite unsuitable for my life style. It's a very common situation. We've probably all got an expensive white elephant hanging in the wardrobe which we'll never wear yet can't bear to part with. In my case it's a beautiful evening dress I wore *once* to a ball and which would look ridiculous on me now. Fortunately my granddaughter has her eye on it and she'll probably wear it, when it fits her, to the local disco.

If you don't want to give your clothes away, there are also the shops that specialize in secondhand clothes, and which pay quite good prices for them if they are in good condition and in beautiful fabrics. As for the style, that's a matter of personal taste and there are devotees of every fashion era ready to snap up interesting clothes.

There are always some things we hang on to because we love them and hope that, even though they're out of

Right: The seemingly effortless elegance of Jean Muir is something many of us admire but hardly dare to think we can achieve. Like the clothes she designs she has her own uniquely individual style and it takes not only knowledge of exactly what suits her, but tremendous confidence to carry it off. Her make-up is stylised, her superbly cut hair uncompromisingly simple and both are a perfect foil for the severity of her colour scheme – she only ever wears navy blue.

date now, they'll come back into fashion. Some will, and you should pack them carefully away. But do look at them very critically. Are they, truthfully, so worn out that they'll just look plain shabby when the fashion returns?

Try on every garment that you are thinking of keeping. Remember that we change *shape* over the years, even if our size and weight remains the same. What once looked attractive just isn't flattering anymore. It's usually shape, rather than age, that governs what we should wear.

My friend Maureen Baker, who makes clothes for Princess Anne and other members of the Royal family, told me why. The roundness of the stomach rises *higher* as we get older and she says she often has to alter the shape of skirts to allow for this by dropping the waistbands on to the hipline and so avoiding that pulled-in look at the waist which accentuates the stomach. 'And don't wear centre front fastenings either,' she warned. 'They just pin-point the bulge.' I have several pairs of trousers which still fit me perfectly well but which unfortunately can't be worn anymore because the centre zip fastening makes my stomach look too big.

Once you have whittled your wardrobe down to the items you really wear, you are in a position to see what it is that you *need*. As a guideline I am going to tell you what I consider the essentials to be. You can then decide what, if anything, you *want* to add.

THE BASIC WARDROBE

I've based this on my own experience of having to attend special functions — day and evening — at very short notice at any time of the year. If you too design a skeleton wardrobe of nice items that go together, panic about what you're going to wear should then be a thing of the past. It is best to aim for dateless, classic clothes, with a selection of eye-catching accessories to pep them up and ring the changes.

This doesn't mean you have to have a *large* selection of 'ever ready' clothes but it does mean that what you have got must be in perfect condition. Clothes immaculately clean and pressed. Shoes and handbags well-polished and in good repair. The very young can, perhaps, get away with a scruffy, thrown-together look. But what marks out an attractive older woman is care and attention to detail with her clothes — without this, elegance is impossible.

You will probably find that you already have many of the items I include in the basic wardrobe. That's good! It means that you can spend your money on the co-ordinating extras that

---

STYLE PLUS

Here are the ten top points to bear in mind if you want to be stylish. Elegance and comfort — feeling completely relaxed in what you wear — are the two main ingredients of style, as these points show.

1. Go for clothes that are loose fitting and comfortable. Elegance is impossible if what you are wearing is straining at the seams, bulging round the hips and thighs or pulling open at the bust. Nothing looks worse than a too tight skirt that rides up when you sit down, or trousers that show every line of the body. If you have to struggle into something, don't wear it. A big woman can look magnificent — but if she is wearing something that is too tight she looks plain fat.

2. Be casual. Wear your shirt sleeves pushed up, showing pretty bracelets or a watch, Shirt sleeves buttoned at the wrist can look matronly.

3. Keep some buttons undone on a suit jacket, or it can look stuffy and prim. In the same way, leave the top button of a shirt or blouse unbuttoned, for a relaxed and confident look.

4. Wear bras made of soft fabric, or sports bras if you want extra support. Don't wear stiffened bras that give you a hard, armour-plated look, or raise the straps so high that your bust is in the region of your chin — nor lower them to down around your waistline. Your bust should be level with the mid-point between shoulder and elbow.

5. Covering up is more alluring

will give all your clothes a stylish edge.

Colour it neutral

When planning your basic wardrobe decide on your basic *colour*. You may look gorgeous in violet, but keep brighter colours such as this for your accessories, like scarves and belts, or for shirts and sweaters. It is best to go for a strong neutral as your 'background' colour. Buy all your main, basic items in this colour.

The most versatile colours are black, navy, grey, brown, cream or burgundy. Most of us look especially good in one of these colours. You may find that one colour already predominates in your wardrobe, in which case you may well want to stay with that.

But remember, it is a mistake to say that you are going to stay with one particular colour because it has 'always suited me'. Your skin-tone and hair-colour change as you get older, and this needs to be taken into consideration. So if you are building your wardrobe from scratch, or have a scattering of each colour and you want to decide which to concentrate on, it is worth spending some time getting it right.

One way to do this is to go 'pretend' shopping. Choose a store where you feel comfortable, with individual changing rooms if possible, and try on a selection of jackets in the basic col-ours. Try and assess which really suits you best. If you know and trust the sales person, ask for a considered opinion. If you have a friend whose opinion you value then ask her advice. As this is going to be the main colour in your basic wardrobe you should be comfortable and feel confident with it.

The Essentials

These are the basic items you need in your wardrobe. I have mentioned the style points that are common to each figure type here, but there are other things to bear in mind according to your own particular figure. Check through the key items, then turn to the more detailed comments for advice about your shape.

The basic dress – the shirt waister

This is endlessly useful when classic in line, and preferably made of wool, silk or cotton jersey. Sleeves should be long or three-quarter length. The most flattering neckline is shirt style, or a lowish round neckline. It can be straight and narrow, worn either belted or loose, or the skirt fullness can come from the hips in soft pleats or a flare. This shape will suit you whatever your size. You can find top quality variations of this style in all the good shops and it can be dressed up for any occasion with pearls, scarves, striking belts, amusing

than revealing all, particularly when it comes to the bosom, tops of arms and elbows, now. If you prefer to wear a low-cut, sleeveless evening dress, then wind a filmy, see-through stole around your shoulders, for cover-up with glamour.

6. Classic clothes can be the most flattering of all, but don't allow them to look dreary. Always add your own touch of originality with a stunning belt, original scarf or striking piece of costume jewellery.

7. The 'good', basic colours like black, navy, brown or grey can make your skin look lifeless. So add colours that flatter your complexion. Collars, scarves or jewellery in brilliant colours are revitalizing. Copy the model's trick of having a selection of chiffon scarves in a variety of colours which can be tucked into the neck of a blouse. Put them against your face to see which is the most flattering for each occasion – day, evening or when you're not looking so good. Don't wear a jewel-coloured scarf without make-up or your face may look washed out.

8. Go for natural fabrics, like silk, cotton and wool – or good synthetics which drape and flow.

9. Change all cheap buttons and belts. Quality ones will give an upmarket touch.

10. Beware of bold prints, unless you are tall. They can so easily overwhelm you and look old-fashioned, especially dresses with long sleeves and busy necklines. A little goes a long way, so choose either a blouse or skirt, and team it with something plain.

costume jewellery or a hat.

The important thing is to have your basic dress in the best fabric you can afford. Other 'throwaway' dresses you may choose to buy matter less.

Out are cheap or garish prints and sleazy synthetics. Cheaper dresses also tend to be skimpily cut, so they won't flatter your figure. If the dress comes with a matching loose-fitting jacket, all the better. This gives you a useful two-piece, enables you to ring the changes and, if plain, solves the problem of a coat in between seasons.

The basic skirt

A plain dark skirt in a good fabric, lined so that it doesn't cling and keeps it's shape, is invaluable for day or evening. It should have some movement, rather than a straight line. Look for fine pleats or fullness falling from the hips, or a simple pleat at the front and back. Cross-over skirts, and those with softly flounced hemlines, for example, suit most women. Mid-calf is the most flattering length for your basic skirt — you can't go wrong with that.

But if you are adding other skirts to your wardrobe you can afford to try different styles: up-date from time to time as new interesting shapes appear. Study yourself in the mirror. If your legs are long and good, then you can wear your skirts shorter. Sometimes certain styles demand a longer length to keep the balance right. This is one of the things you learn when you become more critical, and it allows you to be more flexible in your choice.

The basic trousers

Choose well-cut trousers in an un-crushable plain fabric. They should be long enough from waist to crotch so that they are not tight across the front and your bottom — and don't have the effect of cutting you in half. They should be classic in cut and length. If you have a big stomach problem, choose trousers with unpressed pleats from the waist, side-fastenings, or a shape that sits lower on the hips.

Jeans, I suppose, are really meant for the slim, perfect figure. They are symbolic of the young and they can look awful on us unless we are one of the lucky few who have long legs and a slender body. Then they are stunning, sexy and ageless, particularly when worn with a simple cream shirt. Otherwise if you want trousers for casual wear, well-cut jogging suits and track-suits are up-to-date and comfortable.

The basic suit

This is not absolutely essential, but is the perfect in-between outfit especially if you're tired of wearing a coat. If you feel happy in them, then the most useful are in a plain colour, although small checks or tweeds are perfect for almost all occasions. Boxy jackets are the easiest to wear and you should choose one that can accommodate warm clothes underneath. I don't believe in splitting up your good suit by wearing the top or the bottom independently. It invariably means one part gets shabby before the other, spoiling that well-groomed look that a suit should have. However, instead of a suit, you could choose a plain skirt teamed with a co-ordinated jacket. This would allow you to switch around more, teaming the jacket and skirt with other items.

The basic coat

This is probably your most expensive item and something you wear for about nine months of the year, so it must not only go with most things and be practical, you have to really like it as well.

A classic shape in a plain rather than a patterned material that you can dress up is a good buy. Length is an important detail. Make sure that you try the coat on over a skirt or dress rather than trousers. You can, at a pinch, shorten a coat. But a coat that allows hemlines to show will always look dowdy.

Look out for interesting pocket and cuff details but steer away from over-wide shoulders and huge collars as they date more quickly and are not so adapable. This kind of coat is not hard to find in shops such as Jaeger, Aquascutum, Burtons, Simpsons and Austin Reed, but it's often passed over in the search for something more 'fashionable'. You can add fashion touches with draped scarves, boots, or simply the colours you tie in with it.

The basic raincoat
You don't wear your raincoat so often, so this is where you can depart from your basic colour if you want to. Splash out in a bright colour if that's what appeals: nothing brightens up a gloomy day more than a host of cheerful looking umbrellas and raincoats.

The most useful shape, undeniably, is the traditional trenchcoat which is as much at home in the city as it is in the country, and the older it gets the better it looks. The classic British Burberry is coveted by women the world over and it will always be in fashion. The shape never changes and you'll find copies of it at every price level and in every country. It will last, literally, for years, and if you can afford it there's nothing like the real thing.

I always wear mine for travelling instead of a coat. I have it in the traditional cream colour, which means that it does need cleaning and reproofing fairly often which is expensive but I think it's worth it. It is a very versatile coat – good with brogues and thick stockings or with high-heeled courts and the sheerest of tights.

Accessories
With the main items in neutral colours, and good quality fabrics, you can really go to town in choosing the rest of your wardrobe – in both colour and style. None of the following items have the long life of the basics – and most of them don't *have* to be so expensive, though good-quality always shows.

Blouses and shirts
The one indispensable piece is the classic SHIRT, best worn open at the neck. It is probably the most flattering neckline for every figure. It minimizes a heavy bust, is good on the tiniest figure, and goes with almost every outfit.

Go for the colours you feel happy wearing, either plain or printed. Don't have too much fussy detail, like frills or lots of embroidery. The aim, as always, is simplicity. Round Peter pan collars edged with a touch of lace soften an otherwise plain blouse. Make sure shirts and blouses are long enough to tuck into your skirt, and no longer than hip length if you wear them outside.

The bare minimun you need is two:

TRAVELLING TIPS

You should aim to look cool and well-groomed no matter how long the journey. Dressing quietly and *comfortably* marks you as a seasoned traveller even if you don't usually go further than your local shopping centre.
1. Don't wear anything tight and constricting.
2. Always wear uncrushable fabrics. Natural materials are best, like wool, silk, or cotton that has been made crease-proof, because they breathe and you don't get so hot. Most synthetics don't crease but they do generate more heat so make sure they are loose if you wear them.
3. In hot weather, don't automatically go for light coloured prints. A plain navy, or any mid-tone shade looks cooler, stays cleaner-looking, and stands out amongst all the florals and 'hot' colours that abound at air and sea terminals. A light unlined jacket is smarter than a cardigan, and plain courts preferable to strappy sandals.
4. A raincoat in proofed cotton doubles as a coat.
5. Carry your hand-luggage in a plain coloured hold-all that has handles as well as a shoulder strap. Don't have shiny plastic bags with manufacturers motives on them.
6. You'll lose style points if you wear:
– sunglasses with extravagantly decorated frames in bright colours (black, tortoiseshell or neutral are more stylish)
– touristy hats, ethnic clothes and arms exposed to show your suntan.

one in white or cream, the other in a good contrasting colour with your chosen neutral. (See Charting Your Colours)

Jumpers and cardigans

Jumpers can be a problem. If they are too small or too big they are unkind to any but the smallest figure. I personally prefer a neat fitting cardigan. It breaks up that expanse across the bosom and can be worn open over a blouse. Beware of overwhelmingly large sweaters in heavy knits, or those that have tight, high necklines. Double chins have an unfortunate habit of coming to rest on them. Otherwise look for traditional shapes in lightweight wool with a minimum of decoration. I don't think there's any substitute for pure wool or other natural fibres. I'd rather have one good jumper than half-a-dozen synthetics. If you can knit, so much the better. You can make a stunner from a designer pattern for the price of a very ordinary High Street one.

Shoes

Choose shoes in leather — because it is more comfortable: it 'gives' to the foot. Synthetic uppers are very tiring to wear. Your most-often worn basic shoes should always be in leather, though you could have some 'fun' shoes in synthetic materials and unusual colours if you don't plan to wear them for any length of time.

The most flattering shape of all is the medium-heeled court shoe. Two pairs are the minimum: in a dark and a light colour. If your chosen base colours are burgundy or navy, black shoes are fine. Dark brown also looks good with burgundy, as well as the brown base colours.

Handbags

Your bags should also be made of leather. The most dateless handbag is classic in shape and of medium size. Watch out how you carry the classic handbag, though: there is a right way and a *very* wrong way that looks matronly (see the Walking Tall Chapter). It is good to have a handbag that matches one of your pairs of shoes, though black and neutral will tone with almost everything. Don't have a white handbag.

Shoulder bags look relaxed and allow more freedom of movement, and are the only style to wear with trousers.

Huge, cumbersome 'shoppers' are the dowdiest bags of all.

Gloves

Choose gloves in leather to match your shoes and handbag, or in your basic colour. If you wear gloves in summer, well-stitched cotton in a neutral shade is the best choice.

Hats

Luckily, *having* to wear hats is a thing of the past. Except for certain occasions, it is entirely up to you whether you wear them or not. Older women were always being accused of wearing dreary hats so, if it's true, let's stop wearing them.

Hats should lift and enliven your face as well as your outfit. If you like a hat for everyday wear, a flattering shape in which you feel relaxed and comfortable is a must. A brim is often more flattering than a toque which has a rather elderly image.

Fur hats are always flattering. They make a pretty frame for the face and they have the bonus of making the skin look warm and glowing.

Berets are great if they suit you, and they come in a variety of shapes and colours at inexpensive prices. They are youthful — cheeky somehow, and I collect them as I collect scarves, experimenting with wearing them at different angles.

For smart occasions there's no need to play safe with your hats. A bit of frivolity from time to time is fun. But don't wear a heavy felt hat with a summer dress. You can just about wear a light dressy hat with winter clothes

Right: This was taken at my daughter Vida's wedding a couple of years before my fortieth birthday. I did then what I do now when my hair's not at its best and I need something flattering near my face. I wear a large white fur hat — and it always works!

Berets are very flattering and versatile. I often wore them in my early modelling days and I still do today – although I now have them in a variety of different colours and sizes. It's the cheapest hat on the market!

126

for dressy occasions, but a winter hat with summer clothes looks awful.

Belts

If you enjoy wearing belts, you can never have enough of them. But as a minimum you need at least one each in dark and natural leather. Look out for those with a curved shape. They sit more comfortably on the waist, won't ride up and give a longer line to the body. An attractive gilt buckle adds style, but keep away from over ornamented trimmings in contrasting colours.

A selection of belts in vivid colours is useful for when you want to give an outfit a new look. So is the long-line belt for gently clinching in bulky clothes. It allows you plenty of breathing space without looking like a sack tied in the middle.

Scarves

Some women are scarf addicts and others can't cope with them at all, but I think that they are an indispensable addition to the wardrobe. A brilliantly coloured scarf is the quickest and easiest way to brighten up an outfit and can make it look completely different.

Cotton, wool and silk are best because they drape and flow. Synthetic fibres are inclined to be stiff and rarely fall naturally. Have a selection of plain or patterned, in a variety of colours and look at fashion pictures for ideas on how to wear them. If necessary anchor them with a brooch if they slide about.

I often slip the ends of long scarves, if they are fine and silky and not too long, into my bra if I want them to sit inside a shirt or jacket.

Long warm winter stoles worn round the shoulders are fine as long as they are a fashion item in themsleves. The fashion for fine-wool paisly scarves worn round the shoulders *over* a coat will undoubtably return again and again and gives a wonderfully stylish twist to a coat that you've had for a while.

I haven't found any use for those tiddly, handkerchief-size squares that practically choke you if you try to tie the ends. But long scarves, if cut on the cross, are very adaptable and will drape easily and stay in position however you wear them.

Stockings and Tights

Mid-toned stockings and tights are the choice if your legs are not your best feature. Very pale colours are enlarging, and black 'outlines' the shape, drawing attention to it – *not* slimming as many people believe. Support tights

are a good choice, whatever your legs are like. They can be as sheer as ordinary tights, and apart from the comfort they give, they firm the ankles and thighs at the same time.

If your legs are good, make the most of them. You can really go to town with your stockings and tights. Wear the sheerest stockings, and a hemline that draws attention to them — a flounce or fine pleats are good eyecatchers. Black looks fabulous on good legs if worn with elegant black shoes.

When the fashion is for lacy or coloured tights, then do wear them if you want to show off your legs. Tights and shoes in toning colours make a real impact as long as they are not in glaring colours.

YOUR EVENING WARDROBE

If your social life demands a lot of dressing-up then it is worth investing in fabulous evening gowns. But most of us (and I definitely include myself!) want to be able to look glamorous and dressed up without going to a lot of expense.

I believe evening wear should be fun — and generally I don't think it needs to be as 'good' or expensive as day wear. Gatherings in the evenings are usually crowded, with subdued lighting. No

Plain tights worn with court shoes will make your legs look longer, whereas strappy shoes and patterned tights will make them look shorter

TAKING CARE OF YOUR CLOTHES

1. De-fuzz little round bobbles of wool on your jumpers with a fine wire brush. Or pull them off with strips of sticky tape.
2. When ironing, use a fine water spray or a piece of muslin rung out tightly in water.
3. Always iron delicates under a cloth.
4. Don't iron creases down the sleeves of your blouses. This is for men's shirts. Use an ironing pad or sleeve board.
5. Don't press a crease in the neckline of your shirt. Iron the collar, and down the front neck on the inside, and the collar will fall naturally into place.
6. Never press the rib of sweaters.
7. Always use shoe trees.
8. Dry wet shoes with crumpled newspaper inside, away from direct heat.
9. Polish shoes before each wearing, and have them re-heeled regularly.

one has the time or the inclination to examine minutely what you are wearing – the impression is all. That's why expensive little black numbers often get totally lost. A little inexpensive glitter and dazzle to make you stand out is a much better choice – but be careful not to overdo it!

A full or three-quarter length black skirt is really all you need as a basis for your evening wardrobe. You can look different in it every time. Make sure it has plenty of softly draped fullness, if possible with pockets in the side seams. An alternative is a pair of black evening trousers in a silky fabric. The thinner the fabric, the more loose-fitting and comfortable they can be without emphasizing your shape.

Have at least one really gorgeous blouse for extra-special occasions. As I say, it doesn't have to cost a fortune. Gold lame, embroidered lace, sequined jackets, glittering lurex all look good at night, so don't pass these over when looking for something to team up with your evening skirt. A pure silk blouse (or silk or satin look-alike) in a brilliant colour is effective under the hard artificial light that sometimes shines in the evening.

'Junk' jewellery is quite permissible. The fashion for chunky brass-effect jewellery which is patently fake, but looks wonderful under artificial light for evening use, is an example.

You can afford to be more playful with evening shoes, though the best choices are probably black satin, gold or silver.

A clutch bag for evening is all you need – pare down the things you believe you *have* to take out with you, so that you just have the essentials.

SHOPPING GUIDE

Whether it is to buy your basic wardrobe, or to supplement it, you can't get away from shopping. You either love it or hate it – I do both. Bitter experience has taught me some do's and don'ts to bear in mind when shopping.

● When buying trousers, sit down in them to make sure they're comfortable.

● Dressing room mirrors are notoriously unflattering, so prepare yourself for the worst by wearing make-up. The only good thing about them is that you look positively glowing by comparison in your own mirror at home. I'm sure they place mirrors in the most unflattering light – so that you buy more things in the hope of looking better!

● Make sure that what you buy fits you properly. Check that shoulders are wide enough and come to the outer edge of your arm – lift your arm and see whether it pulls at the shoulder. If a coat or dress is fitted make sure that the waistline is on your waist and not above it otherwise you will always feel uncomfortable and you'll look uneccessarily short-waisted. If you can't get dresses long enough in the waist, then choose separates or an unfitted dress that you belt yourself.

● Check your back view to see that skirts don't ride up over your bottom and that the hem is even. If something is more than a few inches too long for you check carefully that the rest of the proportions are right. Clothes are usually made in a variety of lengths so you don't have to get the wrong size.

● Check the colour of everything you buy next to a window in natural light. That peachy colour you selected in the shop could look positively orange in the daylight.

● Look for signs of quality: coats, jackets and skirts well-lined; deep hems – which don't show from the outside; smooth, unpuckered sleeve insets; even hemlines; pleats deep and not skimpy.

● Bad signs: loose threads, uneven stitching – particularly on dresses and blouses; button-holes unravelling.

● Check the 'care' label before buying: do you want to keep dry-cleaning your cream suit? Do you let your hand-washing pile up? Buy garments that you are willing to take care of in the way suggested, otherwise you won't get the wear out of them.

● When buying coloured shoes or bags, always buy the correct colour polish at the time.

● Don't be rushed into buying. Only shop where you have a full-length mirror in the dressing room, and one that enables you to see your back view. If the saleswoman worries you by hovering around ask her to leave you alone while you make up your mind.

● Ask a friend's opinion by all means but *you* should make the final decision. When going on a shopping expedition only take a friend if she's sympathetic to you.

● Don't succumb to sale fever. Just because something is reduced or cheap doesn't make it good value. Is it an item you needed or wanted anyway? If so, check the label: buy names you know and like. Many shops buy in low-quality items specially for the sales, and you should avoid these.

● Check sale items that have been on display, for fading. If they have been in the window they may be lighter across the shoulders.

● Check the seams of sale items. If they have simply come unstitched , that's fine. You can easily mend this. If they are torn apart, leave them.

● Check a sale garment *all over* for stains.

● Check yourself full-length when buying a hat.

CHOOSING THE RIGHT CLOTHES FOR YOUR SHAPE

The basic rule of dressing well is knowing your shape. Most of us don't need to be told what's wrong with our figures — we've lived with them long enough!

Thank goodness nobody is perfect! I learnt that fact when I was a model-agent representing some of the most beautiful girls in England. 'She's too short-waisted, too long in the bottom, her bust is too small (or too big), her shoulders too wide, her neck too short etc.' were daily complaints from dress designers and manufacturers. Figure-faults were never a problem for the photographers — the camera is more critical of the face than the body.

But models are in the business of looking good and they are adept at camouflaging their shortcomings. The tricks they use are useful to all of us.

Too many books on looking good start with the idea that you are going to diet, exercise or otherwise remould yourself into the 'perfect shape'. That is impossible — even if you wanted to. You don't have to have a perfect body to look marvellous. It's just a matter of knowing what to play down and what to play up. That's why in this section I am going to pin-point the most common figure-faults, and tell you how professionals deal with them. See if you recognize any of your so-called shortcomings in the list that follows.

Short and plump
● COAT. Have movement in your clothes. If your hemline is narrower than your shoulders then you're going to look top heavy. Choose unfitted coats with fullness coming from the hips. A straight, tightly buttoned up coat is unflattering.

● BIG BUST. If your bust is big, don't wear high necklines. A shirt collar is best, or a low cut Peter Pan. Keep away from tight-fitting sleeves that accentuate heaviness at the top of the arms.

● DRESSES. One-piece dresses are more flattering and more comfortable than separates. Have them unfitted at the waist and wear them loosely belted. Even if you don't have a waist to speak of, I still think a pretty belt helps.

● JACKETS. Don't wear anything double-breasted. Whether it's a dress, a cardigan or a jacket, it looks too structured and all those buttons look heavy and rather masculine. Clothes should sit comfortably on the body.

● HEMLINE. Don't wear your clothes beyond mid-calf in the belief that it makes you look taller. It can look dowdy.

● SHOES. Wear shoes with a low or medium heel. Tottering about on very high heels accentuates your height. Court shoes can make your legs look longer.

● ACCESSORIES. Don't overwhelm yourself with a huge hat or bag. You can take height, rather than width, in a hat and a slim shoulder bag looks good with your build.

● SUITS. Single-breasted tailored cardigan suits look good on you, especially if they have small shoulder pads in the jacket to square the top. Don't have the jacket too long — just long enough to cover the hips. Beyond that it shortens the figure.

● FABRIC. You look your best in plain fabrics or small prints in muted colours. Spots and small checks are particularly good, but keep away from all-over large vivid prints and anything too jazzy in design. You can still wear bright, eye-catching items, but keep them small.

● SKIRTS. Wear your skirts quite big in the waist so they sit on your upper hip bone. This camouflages the stomach. Alternatively go for elasticated waists. Never have a skirt with a single centre pleat, and have the fullness coming from the hips, not the waist. Pleats should be deep — not skimpy so they pull apart.

● TROUSERS. Yours isn't the best shape for trousers but if you like them and find them warm and comfortable then there are a few things to remember. Don't wear them in bright colours. Dark colours are less obtrusive and you can team up with a colourful top. Don't have them tight at the crutch, or wide round the ankles. Never have a centre zip. They should be loose round the waist and have soft, unpressed pleats over the stomach. Don't choose clingy stretch jersey. Wear them with a loose top which covers your bottom, rather than tucked in. Have them long enough to reach the top of your shoes

---

STYLE DETRACTORS

● Don't wear anything in crimplene — if there's still any of it around! It is the most ageing of fabrics, with no movement. Personally, I'd rather dress in sackcloth.

● Don't carefully match shoes, hats, gloves and handbags. It's too contrived and *not* elegant.

Two of them can match — but not more. Always add a touch of your own. A bright red leather handbag, for example, is clever if you're dressed all in navy.

● Watch the length of your clothes. Don't wear anything that shows your knees, or have hemlines that trail round your ankles. Mid-calf is best and most flattering, whatever fashion magazines may say.

● Never buy a hat sitting down. See yourself full-length to get the overall effect, preferably wearing the outfit your teaming it with, otherwise you might get the balance all wrong. If you are tall and big, don't go for a dolly hat. If small, don't overwhelm yourself with a huge brim.

● Steer clear of gimmicky plastic accessories, no matter how attractive they are.

and wear matching socks. Never wear them too short, whatever the fashion.

Tall and overweight

You may be fed up with your size but you've got plenty going for you! In my modelling days we used to call big girls bold and curvy, and big certainly never meant stodgy. You can carry off the most striking outfits, but, as with every figure size, it's a question of achieving the right balance. You need a good shoulder line to begin with and it should be as wide as your hips. This doesn't mean huge ugly padding, but clothes cut wide across the shoulders, and also big enough to allow for width across the bust and plenty of movement. You don't want to look as if you've grown out of your clothes.

● SUITS are good on you. Jackets either single breasted or boxy. Skirts with a good swing to them.

● COATS. You can really be bold here. Large swinging styles – capes are good – with collar details and distinctive pockets. Apart from that don't wear anything with a military flavour – epaulettes or tabs on the shoulders. You can carry off tweeds, bold checks and plaids splendidly.

● DRESSES can be loose and flowing or fitted, and the more showy the sleeve, the better. Be careful when choosing flowered prints as they can be too much of a good thing. Shiny fabrics are enlarging. The best fabrics are matt jerseys, in dark or good strong colours that you can dress up with accessories.

● NECKLINES. If you have a long neck you are spoilt for choice. Soft cowls and large collars and cleverly draped scarves are better than little round collars. Open shirt collars are always good.

● TROUSERS are fine providing they are in plain dark colours, and are plenty long enough. They can be straight-legged or looser. Like most trousers on older women they shouldn't be tight and clingy with centre zips, but should have soft tucks over the stomach. If your bottom is large, or your stomach, then don't tuck in a blouse, but wear it loose. Ideally have an easy-fitting tailored top, buttoned down the front, reaching to mid-thigh.

● JUMPERS. I don't think the traditional English jumper looks good on you unless it's under a roomy matching cardigan. Think in terms of jersey blouses with a shirt collar.

● SKIRTS. With your height you can wear your clothes longer than mid-calf, but beware of having them too long.

CHARTING YOUR COLOURS

Clothes should be colour-linked for maximum style. Have a neutral shade as your background and introduce contrasting colours in your shirt, jumper, handbag, gloves, scarf, or hat – but the secret of elegance is only to contrast one or two of them. As a general guide always wear the colours that make you feel good.

Here are some excellent colour combinations. Look supremely elegant – and play safe – with the first suggestions under the base colour. Be bold and eye-catchingly stylish with the suggestions beneath

NAVY
Safe: white, pale pink, cream, peach.
Bold: gold, emerald, cherry red.
GREY
Safe: white, pale lilac, pale pink, pale blue.
Bold: scarlet, royal blue, buttercup yellow.
BROWN
Safe: white, cream, pale yellow.
Bold: egg yellow, bright navy, acid green.
BURGUNDY
Safe: white, camel, pale peach
Bold: shocking pink, lime green, electric blue
BLACK
Safe: white, cream, pale silver
Bold: all the bright primaries.

Pleats are good if the fullness comes from the hips. Straight skirts are hard to wear unless they fit really well, or have a centre or side pleat. In any case always have them lined so they don't seat.

- SHOES. Don't go for flattees just to make yourself look smaller. Even the smallest heel looks better and it's hardly your fault if others are smaller than you! Copy the Princess of Wales and don't make concessions to your height.

- HATS. You can really go to town on large eye-catching hats with big brims and not look overpowered. What you shouldn't wear is something small and insignificant.

- HANDBAGS. Keep them big and eye-catching. Don't be tempted by slim line clutchbags except for the evening. With your build, the right balance is the important aim.

The 'Average' Figure
This usually means you are around size 12 or 14. That is, a 36 to 38 bust with hips about two inches bigger. Height between 5'4" and 5'6". Most manufacturers use these basic sizes so you'll be well-catered for. Which isn't to say you don't have your figure problems the same as the rest of us. I've listed the most common ones below.

- HIPS AND BOTTOM. If your hips are the biggest part of you – which is the famous English pear shape – then they look best under a skirt. Pleats from the hips are good as they are fluid in line and have a wide hemline. Don't wear gathers at the waist and keep your belts narrow and on the loose side. Pockets are better set into a side seam. Don't wear clingy fabrics and preferably have your skirts lined or wear a firm underslip.

- LARGE BUST. First and foremost, make sure you have a well-fitting bra.

Avoid high necklines. V-necks and shirt collars and lowish round necklines are the most flattering. Never wear tight-fitting jumpers of any kind. Cardigans are good because they break up the bodice line. See that armholes aren't too tight. Side darts on bodices give a better shape and more freedom of movement. Jackets are kindest when single breasted with long revers and low buttoning.

- SMALL BUST. You've probably often moaned about being too small but it's by far the easiest to dress and it does keep it's shape longer! Clothes generally look better on a small size but there are still pitfalls. A small bust can mean narrow shoulders, so it's worth putting small shoulder pads in blouses and dresses. Don't wear tight fitting jumpers – they don't look any better on a small figure than they do on a large one. You can wear draped and gathered tops, twin sets and either fitted or loose jackets.

- BIG STOMACH. Oh dear, the bane of our life! I don't think I've ever come across a woman who hasn't thought her stomach was far too big. There are lots of dressing 'do's and don'ts' worth following.

Don't wear gathered skirts with big patch pockets or stripes.

Don't wear centre zips as these emphasize the bulge. Trousers shouldn't really be worn either but if you can't resist them, then make sure you wear an over-blouse or sweater.

Don't wear straight tight-fitting skirts. Nothing looks worse than a skirt that curves in under a too-big stomach. Skirts with elasticized waists are excellent, and so are soft pleats or fullness that comes from the sides with just a little fullness in front.

Don't wear clinging, stretch jersey. Woven fabrics sit better especially if they are lined.

Do wear loose-fitting blouses or a jacket to the upper thigh as a cover up.

Do wear wrap-over dresses, they are very kind to the figure and needn't be in the least bit matronly. A friend of mine with a real tummy problem gets hers from the maternity departments in the smarter stores! She shops quite without embarrassment. She goes in as a granny ostensibly looking for something for her daughter-in-law who is far too busy to come herself and she tries them on for fit! She says she's bought more stylish clothes from them than from large-size departments.

Do wear eye-catching detail on collars or bodice as a good decoy — and padded shoulders help to give a good balance to the figure.

- SHORT NECK. If you sweep your hair up and off your shoulders your neck will look much longer. Don't wear high necklines, especially not polo collars. Shirt necklines, V-necks and low round collars are all good at giving an impression of length. Don't wear embroidery on the shoulders or have exaggeratedly high or padded shoulders. Stud earrings are better than drop, and long beads give length. Don't wear a choker.

- LONG NECK. If you prefer not to keep your neck on show now, there are many things you can do. You can wear low polo collars, pretty scarves, or lovely stoles. Large collars are good and you can have them as elaborate as you please. Keep away from anything too revealing, like low-cut necklines, deep unbroken V's and collars cut away at the sides. Some apparently low-cut dresses and blouses also have additional filmy, see-through gauzy fabric across the bust and up the neck. This is a very good compromise.

Chokers or many strands of pearls are preferable to a single long necklace, and large extravagant earrings can look very good.

- HEAVINESS AT THE BACK OF THE NECK. Wear soft gathers or tucks at the shoulder line or let a small scarf fall casually over your shoulders.

- SHORT WAISTED. Short waisted means being short from shoulder to waist and if you have a heavy bust as well, this can leave you with little space for a waistline. Wearing shoulder pads lifts your clothes and is a great help in giving you extra length from shoulder to waist. Don't tuck in blouses or jumpers, wear them over your skirt, about two inches below the waistline. Never wear wide belts — they will shorten you even more — choose narrow ones that are shaped and curved. They will give a longer line to the back. Keep pockets low down on your skirt and don't have gathers from the waist. Lowish necklines are kinder than high ones as these are inclined to emphasize a short waist.

- NO WAIST. Don't give up wearing belts even if you haven't got an indentation any more. A narrow belt worn under a loose open jacket gives the illusion of a waist that goes in, and an eye-catching buckle can make it an important feature. A shaped belt is better than a straight one which will always be inclined to ride up. Don't wear wide belts or be tempted to make yourself look smaller by pulling yourself in tightly because it will have the opposite effect. It will also be terribly uncomfortable! I remember how awful it was wearing a waspie in the 1940's when I was modelling. I had to get myself down to a nineteen inch waist and the effort practically ruined my digestion for ever. Better no waistline than that misery!

- PROBLEM ARMS AND SHOULDERS. If your arms are no longer your best feature, you should wear sleeves that reach at least to the elbow, or to the wrist. Keep them quite full and gathered in to the cuff, or rolled up to mid-forearm. Don't wear sleeveless tops. The top of the arm is an area we should keep covered up.

If your arms are too heavy, make sure your shoulder seams are wide enough and come right to the edge of your shoulder. If you're round shouldered, put shoulder pads in all your clothes. When wearing long sleeves, don't have them tight and sausagey. You can wear sleeves just below the elbow because a plump lower arm is pretty, but don't wear anything sleeveless.

UNDERGARMENTS – FOR ALL FIGURES

If you've ever struggled into side-zipped boned corsets, waspies or suffocating harnesses, the present day figure-controllers are a pleasure to wear. The soft, two-way stretch fabrics firm and control the body but also allow movement and comfort. There's a choice for every figure – but have them fitted professionally if you can.

● Even if you're slim, your muscles may still need a little support for a smoother line. If so, either a panty girdle or a girdle with suspenders is all you need.

● If you need all-over control there are all-in-one girdles which have stretch and woven panels to hold you in where you need it. Make sure they are long enough to cover any thigh bulge, and that they are not too tight across the waist or cut into the crotch. If you wear trousers, then these must be loose enough not to show the line of the girdle underneath. Suspenders that show through are worse. If you wear trousers a lot invest in a good pantie girdle.

● Bras should have quite wide comfortable straps if you're on the heavy side. Thin ones have a way of cutting uncomfortably into the flesh. Don't wear the natural-look bra – that means one without any shaping on the cup as they have practically no support of any kind. Make sure, also, if you have full soft breasts that the bra fits well, with no overflow at the sides.

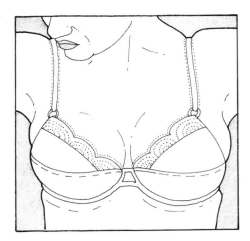
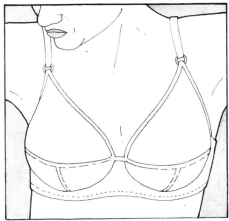

QUESTIONS AND ANSWERS

I need an all-purpose wrap that will take me anywhere in the evenings, and go over everything long or short. Does such a thing exist?

If you are not able to find what you want in the shops, you can pick up an idea from Liz Emanuel, the top designer. She has made herself a black cashmere wrap from a huge square with a centre slit, the edges bound to neaten them. She slips it over whatever she is wearing, slings the ends round her neck and snuggles up inside! You can look for fine wool remnants so that you can make several in different colours.

Can you suggest a practical but elegant outfit for a working woman who has to travel a lot, yet must always look good?

A coat for all seasons, such as a Burberry trenchcoat is a must: it looks as good in the sun as it does in the rain. It has a casual, but expensive look, and you can introduce colour with a selection of scarves.

Under it a well-tailored suit, that has a feminine rather than a masculine cut. It should not be tight in any way, so that you can work, walk and sit comfortably while you are travelling. Tailored shirts, but in soft expensive fabrics, such as silk, are good worn underneath, or a quietly printed blouse. Mrs Thatcher, who spends a lot of time travelling and attending fuctions, says that the beautifully tailored suit is the backbone of the executive woman's wardrobe. For accessories, have the best leather court shoes, handbag and gloves that you can afford.

Mrs Thatcher always looks *essentially* correct *in the way she dresses, whatever the occasion. I've never seen a photograph of her where her clothes are creased after long hours of travelling or cumbersome, or when she is ever anything but beautifully groomed. She reflects perfectly the successful, confident career woman, and at the same time she likes to have something soft and feminine at the neckline.*

Maureen Baker, who has made clothes for Mrs Thatcher for all kinds of formal occasions says, 'Her style is totally her — her clothes reflect her personality. She keeps to a definite recognizable line but is interested in fashion and she has her clothes updated. If something suits her she will have it repeated in other materials. I always put pads in her shoulders to balance her figure.'

137

I am very tall, and it is no consolation to know that models are too. What can I wear to make me look shorter?

What you should aim to do is soften your silhouette. Severely tailored clothes without any softness or flow accentuate height. Plenty of movement in your skirts – pleats, gores, flounced hemlines will help.

Wider shoulders have a softening effect, and three-quarter jackets are good, as are wide belts – interesting detail that breaks up your length.

Choose interesting collars and different sleeves. These draw attention sideways, rather than up and down.

Don't let your handbag hang by its handles – tuck a large, eye-catching clutch bag under your arm. This will also break up your height.

Two-colour combinations are good, but keep the most dramatic colour for your lower half.

You probably wear flat heels – if you do, make sure they are pretty pumps, with at least a one-inch heel.

If you like to wear costume jewellery you can affort to wear eye-catching pieces: chunky bracelets, for example, and stud – not drop – earrings.

If you wear a hat, keep it wide at the sides, and not high on the crown.

I'm very long-waisted and have difficulty in finding dresses that fit. Most waistlines come somewhere around my ribs. What is the best style to look for?

I have the same problem, so most of the time I buy separates, which allow the skirt to sit on the natural waistline.

Almost all the cheaper clothes are cut for shorter waists. You can help matters by cutting off any belt loops and wearing an extra wide belt to cover the waist join. Alternatively, buy unfitted dresses and belt them yourself.

Fashion houses such as Jaeger and Susan Small design for the longer waisted woman.

I love knitted hats, but they look so flat on the crown, as they have no stiffening. Do you have any helpful suggestions?

You can buy canvas hat shapes in haberdashery departments to give them body. Other wise, you can fold a scarf inside to give them extra bulk.

I practically live in black but I feel drab in the evenings. I don't like wearing scarves, so it's back to my double row of pearls. Any suggestion?

Lotte Berk also loves wearing black and rarely changes her colour scheme. But, as she says, she loves to be noticed and admired. She has a couple of sequinned cardigans that she wears over a simple black dress. This is the only concession she makes for the evening.

Mavis Nicholson, the TV presenter, also says she has a glamourous black sequinned jacket that has been her standby for years. Perfect for adding a touch of glitter to 'what-the-hell-am-I-going-to-wear' occasions. She wears it with her black skirt.

I'm a size 16. Does this mean I can never wear shiny fabrics such as satin, which I adore?

I've asked Maureen Baker about this, and she said that shiny materials can look great on larger sizes providing the fabric is not synthetic. 'Pure silks have a natural, fluid gloss which drape the body,' she says. 'Of course the style must be right and generously cut so that it skims, and doesn't cling to the body.' If you are making up shiny fabrics yourself, Maureen suggests that it is safer to make a long evening skirt or wide, draping trousers than a dress. Alternatively, you can wear the fabric as an outer garment, such as an evening coat.

Photographs were supplied or are reproduced by kind permission of the following:

Jerry Bauer 94; Kate Feast Management 34; Granada Television 20; Ivor Kimmel 124; The Press Association 12, 87; Rex Features 18, 43, 47, 96, 119; Felix Schmidt 14; Syndication International 49, 107, 108, 120; Times Newspapers Limited 31.